WHILE YOU WERE AWAY

WHILE YOU WERE AWAY

THE DREAMS 2020 LEFT BEHIND

K.C. BONILLA

NEW DEGREE PRESS

WHILE YOU WERE AWAY

The Dreams 2020 Left Behind

Artwork by Aleksandra Mandic

ISBN   978-1-63676-874-8   *Paperback*

         978-1-63676-964-6   *Kindle Ebook*

         978-1-63730-069-5   *Ebook*

This book is dedicated to my parents, Miguel and Reyna, and my younger siblings, Juan Miguel, Nataly, and Joshua. Este libro se lo dedico a ustedes, mis grandes amores. Sin ustedes, no estuviera donde estoy.

CONTENTS

———

INTRODUCTION

———

IN THIS BOOK, YOU'LL NOTICE STORIES WILL REPEAT THEMSELVES.
This idea started with a set of letters I wrote to myself in college during a freshman Ignatius Retreat's guided practice. I hadn't considered myself very religious—and still remain more spiritual—but that's likely why I cried two years later after reading my first.

I had considered myself a happy person, and I still wouldn't change anything about my life.

But my first year in college forced me to face a lot of ghosts. Ghosts and hauntings have always been part of *Latine* culture (e.g., Día de los Muertos and La Llorona). However, there was a difference between living in folklore and facing painful wounds that never quite healed. As a third year, I read letters from my freshman self who hoped the future "her" would be more grounded in wisdom, that her fears of separation would be relieved, and she would be happy again.

That freshman wished she could address the pains from her history, the unnamed trauma.

As a second-generation immigrant, I lived in a different America. I didn't know anyone who had experienced life differently: life had always meant one foot in America and another in the motherland. Being "othered" didn't happen until college, where I was different for my background, my poverty, and my pronunciation of "pizza."

I began to ask questions about why I was lucky to avoid these moments of "otherness" as a child. I sought out podcasts, books, articles, and music, yet nothing quite answered my questions.

Then, the pandemic struck. I began to write letters again, though this time they were addressed to a significant other; but much like my previous letters, they later evolved as conversations to myself.

YOU'LL NOTICE DREAMS WILL REPEAT THEMSELVES.
From those early letters during the pandemic, I understood a simple principle: everything changed for everyone, but no one would come out the same way at the end of it. People of the same communities, families, and upbringings were forced to accept a new "normal," yet we all rode different boats to brave the pandemic's storm.

The pandemic peeled back a layer on society and quickly revealed which groups were the most heavily impacted by the lack of social safety nets. Occasional news coverage covered the impact of the pandemic on immigrants, but media attention shifted to other topics in a rotunda of chaos in American government. The crumbling resources for low-income, first-generation immigrants became a side note, and the potential impact on second generation immigrants fell through the pipeline of noteworthy coverage.

The "American Dream" is a clear example of how first-generation immigrants are crucial to the development of second-generation immigrants, who traditionally have a more robust economic attainment and higher education than their parents.[1] Though studies demonstrate the children of immigrants have strong beliefs and attainment of upward mobility over generations, it doesn't take into account access to resources to help overcome the pandemic across different racial groups. The "American Dream" rarely is discussed with the caveat that it is not a final destination and instead is followed with the "American Reality:" the continuous struggle of retaining stability to avoid backsliding into poverty.[2]

Before the pandemic, Pew Research stated scholars of immigration "questioned whether today's immigrants and their offspring will be able to match the high levels of intergenerational upward mobility experienced by much of the immigrant stock of the nineteenth and early twentieth centuries." Looking at trends from 2013, most modern immigrants are non-white, and they inherently face social and cultural barriers. More specifically, in the same Pew Research study, they estimated "about a quarter of today's immigrants (the vast majority of whom are Hispanic) have arrived illegally and thus must navigate their lives in the shadows of the law; globalization and technology may have eliminated many of the jobs that provided pathways to the middle class for earlier generations of hard-working but low-skilled immigrants. The relative ease of travel and communication have enabled today's immigrants to retain their ties to their countries of

---

1   Pew Research Center, "Second-Generation Americans," *Social & Demographic Trends Project,* February 7, 2013.
2   Gillian B. White and National Journal, "How Black Middle-Class Kids Become Poor Adults," *The Atlantic,* February 8, 2015.

origin and may have reduced incentives to adapt to American customs and more."[3] With the pandemic cutting access to resources and programs that attempt to bridge these gaps, it is more apparent than ever this inequity will continue to grow to a new magnitude.

Despite these systemic problems in the US, millions of immigrants and their families pursue the American Dream—a world that is better for their community. These immigration stories don't end once they hit US soil, but they mark a new beginning to a life with opportunity to rise above all expectations. They leave a legacy of tears, blood, sweat, pain, and love behind. This passion and perseverance is *grit*. Angela Lee Duckworth describes grit not as talent but as "having stamina... [and] sticking with your future, day in, day out, not just for the week, not just for the month, but for years, and working really hard to make that future a reality."[4]

These often-overlooked stories covered migrations that expanded past Mexico and are essential to understand how they will impact future generations. It will take many years for these communities to fully recover from the pandemic, and thus recording their histories is crucial to understanding society's role in supporting and suppressing these groups.

But this isn't the first time these immigration stories were ignored.

YOU'LL NOTICE HISTORY WILL REPEAT ITSELF.

When we consider the American Dream is a point of motivation for many immigrant families and communities in American history, it brings further grievance and frustration to see

---

3   Pew Research Center, "Second-Generation Americans."
4   Angela Lee Duckworth, "Grit: The Power of Passion and Perseverance," filmed April 2013, TED video, 6:01.

these groups' achievements and participation is erased. Even in literature, some of the greatest authors in 1918 (Fitzgerald, Faulkner and Hemingway) were absent in writing about the Spanish Flu pandemic, a period when there were huge death tolls and seemingly little empathy.[5] Though painful, discussing and advocating for changes in the systems that cause these hardships call for illustration in literature (and, by virtue, history); the alternative would cloak these structures' work to perpetuate a chasm across various groups.

To put it simply, American history and literature can be weaponized by omitting the history of immigrants in America. "If it is not written, it didn't happen."[6]

Tahseen Shams, assistant professor of sociology at the University of Toronto, explains when threats to social norms occur, immigrant groups are often seen "as the link bringing the threat inside our borders, closer to home," which perpetuate stigma and harassment. Strategies that attempt to counter this stigma include engaging with communities, educating the masses with statistical evidence, and correcting misinformation (in which social media mitigates most of this fear). However, they all center in one specific goal: humanizing the "out group." Building empathy is perhaps the strongest tool we have to avoid scapegoating. Every disease outbreak perpetuates fear of an out group and consequently pushes our primal psychological response to dangerous consequences.[7]

---

5   Susan M. Pollak, "Do Pandemics Kill Compassion?" *Psychology Today,* March 20, 2020.

6   Steve M. Cohen, "Due Process: If It's Not Written, It Didn't Happen," *Psychology Today,* June 14, 2013.

7   Diane Cole, "Why Scapegoating Is a Typical Human Response to a Pandemic," *NPR,* August 29, 2020.

In a time when everyone is calling for normalcy, like I did, I considered this: was life pre-pandemic all that great? Demonstrations and movements in 2020 excelled at having American society revisit existing social institutions (e.g., privatized prisons) and consider eradicating and reimagining social structures; it is impossible to dismantle institutions without considering why they were created, by whom and for whom. As difficult as those ghosts are, it is more difficult to continue to live haunted and afraid. Instead of fearing the unknown and seeking validation, searching, reading, listening, and sharing are the most powerful tools we have to lay these ghosts to rest.

I admit, I don't know much about life. But one principle I've come to understand through my letters, and my own desire for stability, is it's not found where I am comfortable. In large part, this novel has become a collection of notes, excerpts of my own pseudo-memoir, and research that have guided me in understanding why I continue to be haunted. I've let myself sit with this horror, with this pain, and I've let it walk me back to my roots. From there, I've realized recording stories and amplifying voices, including my own, is necessary to live with what follows.

This novel intentionally spotlights second generation immigrants of various backgrounds who grapple with the same fears I had during the COVID-19 pandemic. This text deconstructs how each of us is more than a statistic, more than an anecdote, and more than an afterthought.

YOU'LL NOTICE STORIES WILL REPEAT THEMSELVES.

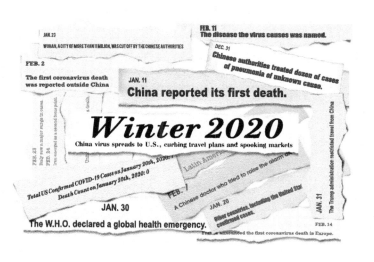

JAN. 23

WUHAN, A CITY OF MORE THAN 11 MILLION, WAS CUT OFF BY THE CHINESE AUTHORITIES

FEB. 11
The disease the virus causes was named.

DEC. 31
Chinese authorities treated dozen of cases of pneumonia of unknown cause.

FEB. 2
The first coronavirus death was reported outside China

JAN. 11
China reported its first death.

Winter 2020

China virus spreads to U.S., curbing travel plans and spooking markets

FEB. 23
Italy saw a major surge in cases.

FEB. 24
Iran emerged as a second focus point.

Total US Confirmed COVID-19 Cases on January 20th, 2020: 1
Death Count on January 20th, 2020: 0

Latin America

A Chinese doctor who tried to raise the alarm

JAN. 20
Other countries, including the United States, confirmed cases.

The Trump administration restricted travel from China

JAN. 30
The W.H.O. declared a global health emergency.

JAN. 31

FEB. 14
France announced the first coronavirus death in Europe.

OLIVIA, SCOTTSDALE— JANUARY 2020

———

One month.

It was one month since she decided to take a leap of faith and move to Phoenix. In ways New York could never adapt to, Phoenix was full of change. There was an energy that came from the city that made it so unique. There was an opportunity to change and be different here. Without ever visiting the city, she took a drunken girl's word on the beauty of the place and took off. Against the wishes of her parents, she decided to ride out the storm in Phoenix and rebuild herself in the place people least expected.

One month.

That's how long she had to find stable footing before her parents dragged her back to face the music in New York. She just needed a bit of time away from it all. Her entire life had been built around the high rises and concrete streets of the Big Apple. Its cold ground had knocked her down hard, and she didn't want to go back until she had a plan. Or at least, until she had some real friends.

One month.

Zero leads for an apartment. It's not like she couldn't pay for an entire studio or house, but… Having a roommate meant she might at least make a friend. And she was desperate for those. Besides, it was a great way to stick one to her parents who purposely restricted her access to extra cash. They had promised to support her move for one month, but after she was on her own. So her hunt for a room continued. Sure, there were options to live near the college towns, but she was over that. This was her do-over year—away from her life in college. She had grown so much and needed to be with mature twenty-something-year-olds. She needed to be near a metropolitan city, where she could both blend in and shine. To prove she was different and to exceed the expectations everyone had set for her.

And she hadn't been able to find a place that quite fit the bill—until this one.

It was a room in a gorgeous apartment in Scottsdale with a beautiful balcony overlooking the community dog park. Close to the city, close to the bars, close to shopping centers, close to the national park. She wanted this apartment. She *needed* it.

She switched earrings three times before deciding on her newly purchased turquoise and coral pair, which complemented her red, paisley maxi dress. She flipped her dirty blonde hair for some added volume before checking her mascara. It wasn't until she slipped her iPhone into her Serpenti bag she noticed the time; she slipped on her golden wedges and grabbed her jean jacket and rushed out of her hotel. She'd had enough sense to drive to Arizona, so at least she didn't have to attempt to snag an Uber.

Even with the climbing pressure to meet Priscila Fuentes at Mixie's Café, Olivia couldn't help but enjoy Phoenix's warmth. New York could never match it. She secretly enjoyed seeing everyone back home posting about the start of winter. Here, she glowed, a subtle tan illuminated her usually pale complexion. It had been awhile since she shared this comfort of warm sunshine without the unbearable humidity. The last time she felt like this was at her mom's summer home in Madrid. How many years had passed since then?

Lost in thought, she passed by the café. As she drove around the block to find parking, she reconsidered going in. Based on the area around the café, she would understand if the local townspeople wanted to tear down the whole thing. It stuck out like a sore thumb among the neatly lined, golden yellow buildings outlined with beautiful Christmas lights and manicured with trees and flowers. Even the rocks were meticulously placed into neat piles, balanced one on top of the other. The bright white store fronts paid homage to a time before air conditioning: the spacious porches were lined with rocking chairs and card tables.

The café stood as an offensive mucus yellow building amongst the picturesque town.

Still contemplating her decision, she saw Priscila's message:

I'm wearing a black shirt with a floral print.

Sighing, Olivia found a parking spot a few streets away. After turning the engine off, she checked her makeup and breath. She winked at herself in the rearview mirror before shaking her head, trying to hide an amused smile.

The café looked even more tacky up close.

There was an awkwardly placed red bicycle on top of the café sign that looked like it was bound to drop at any second. The color scheme wasn't coordinated: the red and pale yellow of the exterior led into an almost lime yellow and burgundy interior. The café was due for at least a few touch-ups: the benches could be swapped for something more stable, and the cheesy see-through table of bicycle parts in the far-left corner near the red couch needed to go. She didn't understand the owner's vision.

The soft crimson hues of Arizona's setting sun enveloped the café with more uniformity than it actually possessed. As Olivia stepped further inside, sweeping her unsightly surroundings for a Hispanic-looking girl from the ad, she noted the interior decor reflected the owners' love for the Tour de France. That explained the odd bicycle pieces but nothing else.

The shop retained that quirkiness she expected in San Francisco. Despite its mismatched aesthetic, she couldn't help but be intrigued: a café specializing in lattes, French baked goods, and Tex-Mex breakfast foods was handcrafted for Arizona. But the hodgepodge of accolades, French decor, and bright colors made her question Priscila's taste in… well, *everything*.

She just hoped the apartment would be worth this tacky rendezvous point.

A petite blonde greeted her and offered her assistance. Turns out, she didn't need it. Priscila's inky black braids made it easy enough for Olivia to find her in a sea of blondes and brunettes. She couldn't help but admire how beautifully they were laced together into a low bun at the nape of her neck. Not a single hair was out of place—which contrasted with her physical appearance.

She looked tired. Her eyes were closed, and she was taking deep breaths. Her almond eyes were traced with black eyeliner while her fawn-beige complexion contrasted against the mauve lipstick she wore.

Olivia noted the Canon camera bag hanging off the chair and giant backpack that lay at Priscila's side. Maybe she was a photography student? If Olivia had learned anything from her time in New York City, it was to always befriend a photographer.

Olivia took a moment before approaching her, a bit apprehensive.

"Priscila? I'm sorry I'm late. I ended up in Old Town by accident."

Priscila seemed startled and stared at her for a moment—making Olivia question if she had the right person. She couldn't stop herself from gripping her bag as she tried to feign calmness.

"Oh, don't worry. I haven't waited long. Nice to meet you, Olivia." Priscila extended her hand to invite her to sit, but she hesitated. "Did you want to grab coffee first?"

"No, I'm fine. I'm trying to cut back to one cup a day, but thank you." Olivia smiled, taking her small Hydro flask out of her bag and placing it on the table.

"How long have you been in Phoenix? From your messages it sounds like you've been looking for a roommate for a while," Priscila said.

Olivia tightened her wide smile. She didn't want to bring her baggage into her only apartment lead. "It's been about three weeks; I'm looking to find a good housing situation that won't tie me down."

"I know the agreement is month to month, but I'm looking to share the apartment for a full year's lease. Would that be okay with you? My old roommate moved to Ohio for graduate school, so I'm looking for a long-term roommate."

"Oh no!" Olivia continued, her eyes wide. "That's not what I meant. I guess I mean I want to make sure I get along with my roommate. But I am looking for an apartment with the intention of leasing long-term—not just a month."

Priscila didn't question her further on the subject, but Olivia caught the subtle scrunch of her face.

"Okay. So what brings you to town? You're from New York and a recent college graduate, right? Is it a job, or are you studying? You didn't really share much about yourself."

Priscila probably had tried to verify Olivia's information and likely stalked her social media accounts. She probably didn't have much to go off of, due to Olivia's carefully curated feeds, and likely had no idea what Olivia did for a living or why she was here.

But Olivia had prepared a short monologue for her backstory:

"Right. So I decided I wanted to move out of New York because that's all I've ever known. I love fashion and design, but I felt so stifled at work. I got this new job that basically helps people get high-end clothes at affordable prices—think second-hand luxury goods. It's not what I want to do long-term, but I'm able to work out of their Phoenix office. I can just live more comfortably in Arizona than New York, but it's also cool to be out in the Southwest. I hope being out here helps with my influencer deals."

Priscila tried to hide her cringe with a sip of coffee. Olivia shifted in her seat and pulled a hair strand behind her ear.

"I know it sounds kind of ridiculous and I'm in the wrong place, but all of the influencers in New York just care about the same styles, same brands, and same threads. I went to Tucson once when I was younger, and I thought it was such a charming little town." Olivia continued, "I thought, 'Hey, I can take in inspiration from the art and local crafts that would showcase our local backyards are just as cool as these metropolitan cities.' I want to be part of this rural revival we are doing in Austin, Montana, Denver. I think Phoenix is next."

"No, I don't think it sounds crazy at all," Priscila said with a strangely high voice. "I really appreciate that. I try to do the same thing with my photography."

Olivia beamed at her and immediately leaned forward. "That means a lot—thank you. What kind of photography are you into? Do you have a public profile you share it in, or is it just a hobby?"

Priscila shared a small smile and tried to brush off her work. "I don't have a portfolio or anything, though sometimes I'll share a photo on Instagram. It's not great work, but I try to capture people in action. I don't really like taking portraits because people get weird about posing and how they look, but I like to capture people weaving or painting murals. There's something about capturing the creation of art that intrigues me. It's just something I like to do in my free time and helps me explore places, old and new."

Reaching over, Olivia laid her hand on Priscila's wrist. "I'm sure it's amazing work. I'd love to see it if you feel comfortable sharing it with me." Priscila's tight smile persisted after Olivia removed her hand. "It sounds like you've lived here awhile—are you from here? Or did you study here?"

It was Priscila's turn to sit a little straighter. "I went to ASU, which isn't too far from here, but I'm originally from Tucson—"

"Wow! You're so lucky! Tucson is *gorgeous*—the neighborhoods are so pretty, and the wide-open spaces are so inspiring. And the weather is perfect! I hate the cold, though winter outfits are much cuter than the summer ones. Anyway, you were saying…?" Olivia couldn't help it—Tucson felt like so long ago, yet it captivated her like no other place ever had. That was another exciting thing about making this work: she could visit her favorite city in the world on weekends.

Priscila looked a bit taken aback by Olivia's obvious excitement and took a moment to recover before continuing. "Right. I think that was it. But glad to hear you like my hometown so much. Where did you grow up?"

Olivia leaned in, holding onto her water bottle, trying to keep her hands busy.

"I grew up in a townhouse on the lower East side. It was nice. I went to public school and eventually my parents sent me to an all-girls college, which I didn't love, but what can you do? I think I was so done with seeing the same old, same old and being constantly reminded I was studying something my parents didn't consider lucrative. I just wanted to leave that toxic environment. Richard and Rebecca are great but can be overbearing, you know? It's tough being the only child. Do you have siblings?"

"Just one." Priscila paused to take a sip of her coffee. "A brother, Vincent. He's studying medicine at the University of Washington actually. He's close to finishing and getting ready to start his residency."

"Are you two close?"

Priscila nodded slowly.

"Yeah, I'd say so. We don't see each other often but we talk and argue like siblings do. He's just way too nice, which annoys me to no end. So sometimes we need to give each other some room to breathe and catch up through my parents. He gets along better with my mom—she's pretty quiet, but she likes talking to him."

"That makes sense. Are you more quiet like your mom, then?"

Priscila's head cocked to the side, but she didn't miss a beat. "Not quite. My dad and brother are very similar, gentle people. But it makes sense since they're in medicine. My mom and I are more alike, but I guess I'm a little more impulsive. We are both very fierce, but what she can do with a look, I do with my words. She doesn't always approve of my behavior, and that's why I get along better with my dad. He is convinced I will do something great, but I just want to retire."

"Amen to that." With a raised water bottle, Olivia toasted with Priscila. They laughed, and Priscila seemed to relax a little.

After a few moments of silence, Priscila cleared her throat and asked. "So what do you do to relax? I used to watch movies with my former roommate. What films do you like?"

Olivia watched as Priscila absentmindedly cleaned the area around her. "I love watching horror films, especially the reveal: the *why* of the crimes, the *who* of the atrocities, the 'will it be stopped?' questions asked by the audience. That's why I hate spoilers. The whole point of the movie is to see the twist ending."

Priscila stopped cleaning. "Really? If a movie relies too heavily on twist endings, doesn't it fall apart? Shouldn't a movie be something that has a great ending but also takes you through a journey you want to watch again and again?"

"I don't follow."

"Like the *Harry Potter* series. I don't really care for them, but—" Priscila began to wave her hand around but stopped when she saw Olivia staring at her, perturbed.

Priscila dismissed Olivia's reaction with a shrug. "Most people are shocked when I say I don't care for the franchise. Anyway… a lot of people enjoy it, right? They watch the series over and over again. But they know how it ends. Because the character's journey is the captivating part of the film. It's not about the ending as much as it's about the character development."

Olivia sunk her body more, dramatically shaking her head. "But the ending makes or breaks the film. In either case, please don't spoil any films or shows for me."

"Fair."

Olivia was really banking on having mentioned her living at the apartment sounding more natural than sales-y. She watched Priscila intentionally take a large sip of coffee.

When Priscila finally put her cup down, Olivia tried to calm herself. She could feel this conversation officially coming to a close.

Priscila wiped her mouth with a napkin before letting her hands rest on the table. "I think you're a good fit, and I'd like to talk about timing. When can you move in?"

"Are you serious? I can move in this coming weekend!"

"I have the roommate agreement in case you want to sign now. As soon as you sign it, I can send the addendum to the lease to the landlord, and I can give you the keys. I'm the master tenant, so you won't be on the lease itself, but you'll be a subtenant and responsible for staying on for ten months. Just double check I have your name right: Olivia Estelle Price."

"That's totally fine—where do I sign?"

Though Olivia offered to drive Priscila back to the apartment in her Mercedes, she decided to "enjoy a walk around their neighborhood." Olivia didn't mind, and figured they'd have plenty of time to bond in the future. She turned up the radio and bobbed her head to the tune of the top forties, daydreaming about how amazing her new life in Arizona would be.

BELEN, LONDON— FEBRUARY 2020

———

Despite the clouds in the sky, the walk along the Waterloo Bridge was still pleasant. Belen couldn't help but think how nice it was to get out of the stuffy dorm rooms and take a meeting on-the-go with Patrick. The wind was slowly starting to build up and causing the waves to crash against the few sailing boats. The setting sun peeked through the clouds and offered a beautiful golden glow to the nearby buildings—the Shard and St. Paul's cathedral on either end of the bridge. As they turned right on the bridge to the street through the Somerset house, a comfortable silence followed them.

"I'm heading back to the States next week, but feel free to contact me between then and now. You'd be an excellent addition to the LSE family—and it would be great to have another Triton in our alumni base," he said.

Unable to contain her elation, Belen hugged Patrick. "Thank you so much! I definitely will. I would love to get feedback on my application essays in a few months."

They were quickly approaching Temple tube station, but Patrick paused to give her an insistent look. "Seriously. Let's keep in touch. Even if it's not LSE related, I'm happy to act as a resource for you."

"I really appreciate it, Patrick. You'll hear from me soon!"

After Patrick gave her a last hug, he turned back when Belen shouted a last farewell. "Have a good rest of your weekend. And enjoy your Valentine's Day with Sandy!"

She gave a last wave and walked in the opposite direction with a grimace. She never knew how to end networking meetings. Still, her awkwardness couldn't dampen her excitement. Checking the time, she knew she'd likely catch Maggie just as she got out of bed. To kill a few minutes, she treated herself to a frap from Starbucks on Kingsway. It was in the direction of her flat near the London School of Economics—and today's meeting called for a celebration.

Letting the red coffee cup warm her redden beige hands, Belen sipped the drink while she dialed Maggie. Not long after, Maggie's uncharacteristically chipper voice chimed through the phone.

"Hey! I was just thinking of you. Happy Friendship Day," her best friend answered.

"Happy Friendship Day to you too, Mags. You're cheery—when did you get up?"

Cracking noises came through the phone line, causing Belen to wince.

Maggie sighed and answered. "Ah yeah, I crashed last night, and I've been awake since six. I even worked out for once."

"And here I am killing time at Starbucks, trying to give you some time to get ready!"

"What happened to you trying to 'immerse yourself completely into English culture' shit you talked about when you came to visit? You're not giving up already, are you?" Maggie's teasing tone made Belen laugh.

"First of all, I still do—I don't even like Coffee Republic, but I'll grab a cup of joe from them. But I wanted to tell you I finally met up with Patrick!"

A shuffling sound on Maggie's end indicated she was getting into a comfortable position. Belen knew she had her full attention.

"Patrick... The guy from the lecture hall who also went to UCSD and got into the LSE program you couldn't shut up about during winter break? That Patrick?"

"Yup."

Though it looked like it might rain soon, Belen walked out of the Starbucks and turned onto Portugal Street. The crowded street made it difficult to hear Maggie. Belen weaved through other pedestrians and made her way to a massive globe statue at the corner of the street.

"Okay bitch, stop keeping me in suspense and tell me!"

"I did my whole spiel on who I was, what I wanted to do, and I asked him questions about his background, and it turns out he's had a fascinating career journey! He does production work for films, but he has his undergrad and master's degree in Economics. He had a wicked story on how he dropped the interim job he had post-graduation from LSE and decided to move to Los Angeles to do all of this production work he had been doing as a hobby. Now he's been focused on helping underrepresented students land internships in investigative journalism and video production jobs." Belen could hear Maggie's focus shifting away at the sound of a nail filer. "Anyway, he works with a lot of non-profits and he's still super tight with the LSE and UC San Diego alumni clubs. Oh, I forgot to mention he's third generation Italian-American and his father was the first in his family to go to college and was able to support his entire family—"

"So he's basically a woke White guy?"

As Belen shook her head, she realized she had stopped walking and stood surrounded by red brick buildings, practically alone in front of the Old Building and the giant globe. The crowds had dispersed leaving the square to her and a few stragglers, pigeons pecking the ground in search of food.

"Well, yeah, but it's more than that. He's genuinely interested in supporting younger students like me to graduate on time and pursue our career ambitions. He thinks I'll be a 'shoo-in' for the master's program."

"Oh my god, Bels. That's great to hear! So what's next?"

"He was pretty insistent I reach out to him about LSE grad applications. He mentioned he was working on a side project and would be busy, but he really wanted to offer as much advice and support as he could to help me."

"That's awfully nice of him. What did you tell him about yourself? He seems super invested—as he should be."

"Just the usual. Y'know?" Still standing in front of the Old Building, she visualized her dream aloud. "I plan to graduate top of my class at LSE and take my first steps to pursue a career as a diplomat and serve my country. Setting a good example for my brother and other kids in my neighborhood; showing them a girl from the Valley can make a massive impact. That there's no mountain without a valley and I've lived through both. But above all, taking care of my mom and brother so they don't have to worry about money. Taking care of them is my ultimate goal, and if I can maintain that stability, I can die happy."

"Well, Ms. Ambassador de León, when you're at the embassy in Hungary, don't forget to fly in your bestie and get her a free ticket for one of those baths in Budapest. Don't forget you're my suga-bestie, and I'm leaning on you to retire when this nursing thing drives me insane and I end up living out of your garage."

"You already know you'll have your own wing in my mansion, Mags." Belen laughed. "And I thought we were both relying on Charlie to take care of us with his engineering degree. Speaking of, what's the plan for today?"

"Oh, don't get me started."

Belen soon regretted getting her best friend started. Maggie always had something new to say when it came to her boyfriend, Charlie. Some days they seemed perfect for each other, and other days they fought over the stupidest things: who drank the last of the milk and didn't buy more, why they weren't invited to snobby Mary's housewarming, who forgot to take care of Doug, their most recently deceased succulent.

The succulents were today's source of frustration. Douglass, Doug's successor, seemed to be doing okay until he suddenly dried out, improved, and drowned. Their plants weren't really the issue—Maggie loved Charlie, but she needed someone who would contribute to the relationship, even if it meant fighting. Charlie was pragmatic and would calculate if something mattered enough to warrant an opinion. Maggie would pick fights and Charlie would assume it was just a phase. It had been going on like this for over a year, and they moved in together soon after their first anniversary—a bold move that offered them some major lessons in adulthood.

Maggie was completely unaware of Belen's dwindling attention span and continued chatting to a less-than-attentive ear. Belen kept circling around the globe, daydreaming of which country she'd like to station at first. Her parents taught her to be brave, so she would take even the most dangerous of assignments. Coming from a military family, Belen felt serving others was at the core of what she needed to do. And though the military didn't call to her, being a public servant felt right—she had an opportunity to change international policies as a diplomat and later, perhaps be the next Madeleine Albright.

Or the first Belen Yackeline de León, US Secretary of State.

She envisioned herself de-escalating North Korea's increasingly dangerous arms race from the Seoul consulate or reimagining how she would have managed American involvement with the 2009 coup d'état in Honduras. While others had fantasies about having their own office, she dreamt of the political influence she could one day possess in hopes of inspiring kids from her community to pursue the same dream.

As she circled the globe once more, she noticed a brunette man in a white T-shirt with red stains circle the globe with her. Belen gathered her overcoat closer to her, confused at the lack of outwear. When she tried to walk faster to see him, he did so as well. If she stopped, she noticed he did so as well. Less than a few feet away with his back to her, Belen felt a pain of familiarity. She continued to circle the globe with him, unable to drive her curiosity away.

Even with the drizzle of the soon-to-be-storm, she didn't seek shelter. Instead, she stopped to put on her beanie to protect her del sereno.[8] It was the sudden vibration that startled Belen into a sharp gasp and consequently, Maggie, out of their conversation.

"Are you getting mugged? Oh my god, call nine-one-one! Wait, is it still nine-one-one in the UK? Doesn't matter—scream 'fire' and not 'rape!'"

Belen read the caller ID of the incoming call. "Mags, I'm okay. My friends are calling me because I missed the climate change protest today. They want me to go out to the Three Tuns to give me the update, and also to make a mockery of the beef ban floating around campus."

"There's a what? What's wrong with beef! I like beef—you remember that YouTube video? That kid went viral!"

"Hun, I know you're very passionate about your meat—"

Maggie's "that's what she said!" went without comment as Belen talked over her.

"But I'm not a part of this meat debate. I'll send you the links though; I need to go. Let me know how it goes with Charlie and if he offers flowers as a peace offering."

"Oh god, he's going to continue to murder plants. The nerve! Yes, I'll let you know what this doofus ends up doing. Love ya."

"Love ya, Maggie."

And though she still felt the growing urgency to drop off her bag at the flat before heading to the local pub, she couldn't help but linger, circling around the globe statue like a metaphor. The man had disappeared. Another text message buzzed and nudged her to start moving away.

When the rain finally came down on its earlier promise, a drenched Belen chugged her coffee and threw it out in the

---

8   Translation: damp night air

nearby trash bin before running back to her flat. Chilled down to her bones, she smiled, letting her daydreams keep her warm.

The rain continued to pour and obscured the view of a gentleman with deep taupe skin, wearing a bright white shirt, covered in blood. He stood still next to the globe in the empty alley. His black pants gave nothing away on his condition, but the slick red tear drop caressing his face melted with the rain pouring on the street.

LEILANI, EMERYVILLE— MARCH 2020

———

"What does it say to do next?"

"It looks like we need to add the egg mixture and… throw it into the pasta?" Leilani reread the article. She had wanted to have a cute *Lady and the Tramp* moment, and pasta sounded simple enough to make. But now she wasn't convinced the author of the recipe knew what they were doing.

Michael towered over her shoulder, his chest inches away from her back. His hazel eyes were on the iPad while her brown eyes were on him.

"Oh yeah, that sounds right. We're done."

Uncooked eggs sounded like an invitation for salmonella, but at least food poisoning would give her a great excuse to skip out on brunch with the girls for the third week in a row. She knew her friends would give her grief, but their brunch spots were always in San Francisco and out of her budget. She knew they would question Leilani's motives. She wasn't willing to admit she preferred to sleep in with Michael and make ugly pancakes instead of paying over fifty dollars in a rideshare to meet up with her friends.

Still eyeing Michael as he mixed the egg concoction with the hot pasta, she closed the cover of her iPad and started to gather the dirty pots and pans to load the dishwasher.

"Okay, looks like this is pretty much ready to eat." Leilani stared at the so-called "meal" and at Michael. "And don't make that face. I promise you it's not another weird 'White person' thing. This is actually how Italians make it. You put raw egg into the mixture."

As she stepped around him to reach for a towel, she pursed her lips in response. *It's still a White person thing,* she wanted to retort, but she held her tongue.

Michael rolled his eyes and nudged her. "You're going to eat it anyway, Leilani. Will you just get in here so we can have dinner?" She let him lead the way, and as he plated the food she refilled their glasses.

Leilani moved to sit on the couch. She regretted buying the IKEA L-shaped couch; instead of adding more space, it made her hunch over awkwardly to grab her plate and glass. She fixed her form-fitting, orange dress as she tried to find a comfortable position to eat and sit with her legs crossed over each other. Michael sat next to her, legs crossed on the couch. She took a small bite of her food, still cautious but more hungry. She secretly enjoyed the juicy ham and cheesy flavors as she took another bite and waited for Michael to finish his mouthful. *The Office* streamed on the television at a low enough volume it didn't discourage Michael continuing his updates on his roommates, whom they had dubbed "Mr. and Mrs. Smith."

"Turns out, she's fighting over the business as well."

"But did she even help build it? Or is she just assuming that being by his side would mean she received funds from it?"

"Who knows? You'd think people who have loud make-up sex would communicate a bit better. But she thinks she deserves some money from the business if they break up."

"Why are they even getting married? It's been almost... three or four months of arguments over a prenup. What makes them think this will turn out well?"

Without looking up, Michael took another large bite. "That's the problem. They aren't thinking. Some people really believe love is enough to warrant a marriage."

Leilani watched Michael nearly finish his food, waiting for him to look up to figure out his odd living arrangement. His fade was already starting to grow out despite his recent trip to the barber.

Once his eyes settled on hers, Leilani spoke up. "How do people even think about getting engaged when they can't figure out how to communicate without arguing? But considering they've only known each other for, what is it now, two years? Two years! Do they just think they are going to figure it out as they walk down the aisle? And you're not even taking into account the whole, 'Hey, my baby momma told me five years later I have a kid,' thing!"

"Shit is fucking nuts. They're both nuts. But I'm glad I get to judge them with you. Thank you for the food." Leilani was still working her way through her pasta as he lightly kissed her on the cheek and picked up the remaining plates.

With a lopsided smile and roll of her eyes, she yelled from across the room. "You know we *both* cooked, right? And you can leave the plates. Don't worry about it."

Michael ignored her and put the dishes in the dishwasher. Easily navigating around Leilani's apartment, he ran the dishwasher and returned to the couch with an open wine bottle as she browsed through the movie catalog on Netflix.

"You know what I still can't figure out?"

She gave up the remote and looked at him. Was he referring to the food? His roommates? The virus? Us? The movie *Us*?

He grabbed the remote and plopped down next to her, easily resting his feet on the coffee table—much to Leilani's chagrin.

"What makes a strong woman go for a guy below her league?"

She snorted as she laid back into his draped arm on the couch. "That's what's on your mind? It's the same reason why the reverse happens. People fall in love in unexpected ways."

Michael caressed Leilani's arm. "No, no. Because then it means relationships are purely accidental. That it's pure chance and the characters don't have a say in it, and you know that's not true. Remember Marc Antonio, from Kat's study group? You guys seemed super chummy, but you said you would never date him—"

Leilani interjected, "I wouldn't date him."

He shifted his arm from under her and shrugged. "But why? There has to be a reason people constantly expose themselves to the risk of failure. It's beyond the need for carrying on our genes. Think about it. Why would black widows kill their mate after getting impregnated? Sure, in the olden days, you would see the need for a hunter to protect the gatherer—that's you—and the offspring. But that would play too heavily into the idea we are all simply products of nature sans nurture."

It shocked her how much one book made him start questioning everything. She chided herself for thinking it was a good idea to lend him a pop psychology book for vacation. Next time, she promised herself she would give him something more clinical, like *A User's Guide to the Brain*. Better yet, maybe *A Handbook to Luck* would distract him from discussing whether humanity imagined feelings or if they were actually real.

She turned her body to him, realizing he wasn't prepared to drop the subject until he had an answer he could be satisfied with.

"What makes you think that a woman—"

Michael interrupted, knowing Leilani well enough to figure she'd try to skew the conversation. "Objectively speaking, you can categorize people into a beauty scale. You might not find them attractive, but you can objectively find people who look better than others. Nurture. Well, and some nature."

She leaned on her arm over the couch and waited for him to continue.

Michael stared at her until he realized why she was silent. He grimaced. "I'm sorry. I promise I won't interrupt. Please go ahead."

She stayed quiet for a moment longer as a reminder she wouldn't engage unless he let her speak.

"As I was saying, what makes you think a woman wouldn't value someone 'who is under their league?' I'm guessing 'a league' entails a lot of materialistic and physical qualities, but you need to view a person holistically. You have to have some scenario specifically in mind."

Michael rubbed his stubble, already dark so soon after yesterday's shave. "Why would Willow stay with Dan? She looks like a girl who can get any guy she'd like—and there's plenty of men in San Francisco. She doesn't read as the type of girl who's drawn to drama, but I guess the make-up sex can't be all bad considering you can hear her moaning from our shared kitchen. Dan's cool, but I guess his whole kid situation and pushing this prenup on her seems like a lot to go through as a twenty-four-year-old woman with options."

"They are an unusual case," she admitted. "But for the most part, I would say people determine the relationship they have built with someone is genuinely strong enough to overcome anything. I don't really understand relationships much more than that with, y'know, me being a child of divorce. But one thing I do know is people don't like to think they are wasting time in a relationship. You invest in a person because backing out of a relationship means you've wasted time on them."

He wrapped his arms around her and kissed the crown of her curly 'fro. He nested his chin on her hair, held her closer. Leilani wrapped her arms around him in turn, feeling the warmth of his body.

"I didn't mean to pressure you into a conversation you didn't feel comfortable with," he sighed. "I guess I don't understand why she would be willing to stick around for a guy she hasn't known long and wouldn't necessarily give her the easiest life."

Sensing he wasn't referring to his roommates anymore, she rubbed his arm, playing a bit with his dark brown arm hair.

"Men sometimes have the hardest time recognizing their own worth," she said with a squeeze. "It's frowned upon by society to let men explore that. A lot of people cover up insecurities with false bravado."

She could feel him hold her closer and let go. She moved to refill their glasses and he lightly held her knee and moved to grab the remote again.

He browsed the comedy category on Netflix, and after checking the cast lists, reviews on Rotten Tomatoes, and Leilani's initial opinions on the given summaries, he picked a film.

By the end of the movie, Leilani's head kept falling to the side as she started to lose her battle against sleep. Michael finished notating his review of the film into his phone before nudging her to move into the bedroom.

Leilani staggered into her bedroom and onto her dresser, refusing to succumb to her drowsiness. She grabbed an oversized long sleeve shirt that ended at mid-thigh and a pair of sweatpants. After changing, she squinted at the bathroom light and turned to see her boyfriend smiling at her with a fond gaze.

"What?" She couldn't help but smile as well.

"That shirt just looks like one I used to have a few months ago. I finally asked out this cute girl I met in my senior year of college during the charity move-out drive. She spit out her soda over her shirt after I made her laugh so hard, and I offered her mine. I let her keep it because something told me she was going to keep making spills like that if I was around."

"Mmhmm. I feel like this girl probably wasn't prepared for the tomfoolery you were going to present her with. And anyway, I'm sure the shirt appreciates the new owner. You should, however, be careful on who you lend things to. They might not make it back to you."

She remembered the day when she tried to return the shirt, but he insisted for her to return it on their second date. Every time she tried to give it back, he would sneakily place it in her bag again. When she noticed, he just offered to pick it up on the next date. And so on, until she finally gave up on returning it.

Michael shook his head. He changed into his sweats, ran to the bed, and piled her spare blankets over him.

She couldn't help but roll her eyes. "You're from Chicago. How is it possible you don't know how to handle a bit of cold air? Even I'm not that bad."

"I'm Lebanese. My body wasn't made for the cold. It's why I live in San Francisco. I. Do. Not. Do. Cold." Snuggling deeper into the blanket mound, Michael still managed to poke his face out and stick his tongue out at Leilani.

She tugged at the comforter hard enough she was able to slip into the bed before he fought her for it.

"You're freezing!" he cried.

"You feel like a radiator." She smirked at his attempts to move away. Sticking her cold feet in between his legs, he fell off the bed from the shock.

"My God! Put some socks on!" Leilani laughed and flipped onto her stomach and spread out like a starfish. She heard the radiator awake with a soft whistle before turning to a hum. The lights turned off and the heavy footsteps moved from one end of the bed to the other. Then, the steps stopped.

Michael whined, "Are you really not going to let me into the bed?"

Her smile grew.

The sudden weight of his body made her gasp before she broke into fits of laughter. His hands attacked her armpits and played across her ribcage, making her shriek.

Two strong thumps hit the floor.

They stayed still, trying to get their breathing under control.

"Your downstairs neighbor really hates us."

She pulled the comforter back. As Michael held her to him, stroking her exposed hip, she replied, "Let's give her a reason to hate us even more."

***

The buzz of her phone woke her up. Sighing, she turned over and faced the other side of the bed. The shower was running, and Michael's off-tune singing should have annoyed her, but it was sweet to hear him so happy in the morning.

Hearing her phone buzz again, she decided it was time to face the day.

She read her notifications and then reread them.

Reminders:
Pap Smear on Tuesday, March 18, at 3 p.m.

Text Messages:
Katherine Ames: Shit. Did you hear? Bay Area to go on lock down. Heard from my sister at CDC that it is going nationwide.

Diana Mendez: OMG! My cousin works for the mayor's office.He says they are going to announce "shelter in place" today. Cardi was right! Shit is getting real.

Leilani started to search for "coronavirus US" as she heard the shower handle squeak. By the time Michael walked out of the bathroom, fully clothed and with wet hair, she was riled up and fired off.

"Did you see this?"

Michael used her spare towel to dry his thick hair. "See what?"

"We're going into lockdown. The virus is spreading throughout the US."

"It won't last long. I'm glad we're taking action, but this will likely be a two-month thing." Michael began to pack his clothes and didn't see Leilani's worried look.

"The whole Bay Area is shutting down. I really don't think this is just a two-month thing."

"Well, if the virus is so serious it requires a lockdown, it's a good thing we're in California. But with the whole medical community looking at this thing, it may not be as bad as it sounds. I showed you that Healthline article—Americans are low risk. I know you don't trust the government, but even Trump can't mess up the systems in place that work in preparation for something like this. This is just like H1N1 or the SARS outbreak. It'll pass."

He adjusted his crisp, white collared shirt before he moved to grab his laptop and pack his workbag with his chargers. He assessed his overfilled bag and removed a shirt before throwing it in again and finally deciding to leave it out. He folded it and placed it in the shared drawer Leilani had assigned him one month ago.

Michael felt the heaviness of the silence and said, "Who told you we're going into a lockdown?"

"Diana."

Michael kept packing and opened his mouth to speak again, but Leilani continued.

"And Katherine—her sister works for the CDC."

He stopped and looked at her. She was still sitting up in bed, gnawing on the dead skin on her bottom lip.

"Hey. If anything happens, I'm still here. I'm only a BART ride away. I can stay home today—"

"No, it's okay. It's just between the empty shelves at Safeway and the messages this morning, it feels closer. Like a ghost." She pulled herself into a fetal position. The panic was starting to set in.

She started to scratch her palms. Michael walked over and held her hands and kissed her on her forehead. As they pressed their foreheads together, Michael whispered a small prayer.

They didn't pray often despite coming from devout Christian households, but the sound of his well-intended words made Leilani feel safe. Feeling the weight of time, she kissed him and pulled back. "You're going to be late."

"I'm always late."

"Yeah, but it's BART on a Monday. It's going to be packed."

He grunted but relented. After Michael kissed her goodbye, Leilani took her time to get ready before logging on to work. In an attempt to look put together, she wore an orange lipstick that complemented her tawny skin and grabbed a company sweater to hide her white tank top. She wore her black leggings and turned on her electric kettle.

Though she enjoyed working from home on Mondays and Fridays, she wished Michael was also able to stay with her. Annoyed she felt clingy, she focused on inputting her credentials onto her computer and adding creamer to her coffee. Her phone vibrated once again. Still stirring her coffee, she grabbed it.

Michael sent two images.

Michael: It's getting real. Get extra groceries if you can today. I'll call you tonight.

She stopped stirring.

One image was of a nearly empty BART car, with people sitting as far apart from each other as they could manage.

The second was of a picture of Market Street. Desolate and gray, the financial district looked completely abandoned.

MARCH 24

The United States led the world in confirmed cases.

MARCH 15

The C.D.C. recommended no gatherings of 50 or more people in the U.S.

APRIL 30

Airlines announced rules requiring face masks.

MARCH 16

Latin America began to feel the effects

Prime Minister Boris Johnson move

MARCH 24

India announced

MAY 27

Coronavirus deaths in the U.S. passed 100,000.

APRIL 6

...are.

Cases topped a million, and millions lost their jobs.

Spring 2020
The Four Possible Timelines for Life Returning to Normal

kdown.

The global death toll surpassed 200,000.

APRIL 26

MAY 8
The coronavirus reached France in December, doctors said, rewriting the epidemic's timeline.

MAY 17
Japan and Germany, two of the world's largest economies, entered recessions.

Total US Confirmed COVID-19 Cases on March 20th, 2020: 18,012
Death Count on March 20th, 2020: 277

APRIL 2

MARCH 17

The E.U. barred most travelers from outside the bloc.

LEILANI, EMERYVILLE— MARCH 2020

———

She wished it was always like this.

Well, pandemic aside.

Leilani was well aware the last thing the United States needed was a healthcare crisis, and she hoped she was just being overdramatic. She didn't want to take any chances with doctors, or police officers for that matter—neither had the best track record of protecting Black people.

But again, pandemic aside, she wished it was always like this.

She watched her emails from time to time as she nested further into her couch with a blanket and hot tea.

Life was good.

She scrolled through Instagram until she landed on Katelyn's throwback posts. She took a screenshot and sent it to Michael:

———

Leilani: You know Kat is posting it on her Finsta because it's taboo to post it on IG.

Michael: 100 percent. She got chewed out as it was on IG stories.

She loved Kat but she knew her insistence to go out "one last time" was a risky move. Leilani used Michael as an excuse to avoid attending, but she couldn't help her jealousy. She knew it'd be a long two months of waiting for things to calm down, and even then there was a possibility of a two-week extension.

Still, it looked like fun. And Kat's cross-fit training really showed.

She opened and scrolled for a few more minutes before she turned on Hulu and half paid attention to an email about revising a deck.

The first couple of days, this was the regular rotation: messaging Michael, sharing memes with girlfriends, getting occasional updates from her sisters who were keeping an eye out on her father, half-paying attention to work emails, ingesting as much TV as she could handle, and treating her iPhone as a rotary phone, endlessly scrolling through the same few apps to pass the time.

She probably could have been more productive, but it seemed like any call she joined it was the same "these crazy times we are living in" and "how are you managing?" for the first twenty minutes. Her general distrust for doctors and police overshadowed any optimistic thoughts she had about the shelter-in-place order being lifted anytime soon.

As poorly managed as the government was, she knew the systems in place were equipped to handle a pandemic even if they abused vulnerable communities. There were limits to that level of cruelty. One presidency doesn't simply undo that.

There were safeguards inherently built to prevent total chaos. Which is why she was okay with having her trips planner open on calls, dreaming of all the fun vacations she would have with Michael and her friends.

The weddings, the birthdays, the holiday getaways...

It was a short sabbatical from her normally rushed, normally busy, life.

And she was here to relish it.

***

Most people wouldn't call her naive. Maybe optimistic. Maybe... forward-thinking.

Not gullible, and definitely not stupid.

It really only took almost a month after the shutdown for things to really hit her. Living by herself, she tended to stay to herself, buy food and supplies in bulk, and ignore her neighbors. She lived there for almost a year and she never found out the name of her downstairs neighbor who kept hitting her floor.

It wasn't until she ran out to get groceries she saw how the pandemic was affecting others.

She knew people were going into a frenzy for cleaning supplies because of the shutdown. She studied economics: supply and demand would do this. And when this was over, the market and supply chain would bounce back.

But what if it didn't?

As she stood in line to get into the grocery store, she felt panic fill her. The lines were ridiculous, and it suddenly felt terrifying to have anyone remotely closer to her. It almost made her get out of line and go home to an empty fridge. She willed herself to stay put.

Still, she felt traumatized to have even gone through the social experiment. She had watched her friends in San Francisco go through it on Instagram and Snapchat—she didn't realize it would be quite as bad in Emeryville.

She luckily had prepared a plan for containment once she returned home: she shed each layer of clothing right at the entrance of her apartment and shoved them into a plastic bag. She washed each item of her three weeks' worth supply of food, disinfected her door and reusable bags, and showered.

It wasn't supposed to be like this. After three weeks of consistent group chats, the first signs of bailing started to show up. Kat was busy, and that was normal. But that meant Nia would likely ditch. And eventually so would Brittany. The fun of being a couch potato started to wear on her. She wanted to do something, anything. She picked up baking like every other bored millennial and started with the first *New York Times* recipe: pumpkin bread.

It was... not bad. And it gave her confidence to keep baking.

Carrot cake. Banana bread. Sourdough. Dinner rolls.

It didn't take long before she was sick of carbs and the hobby fizzled out.

But her hands were constantly itching for activity. An early spring cleaning led to more renovations; binging shows led to purchasing more TV subscriptions. Travel plans led to booking flights for the end of the year under the low fare and flexible cancellation policies.

And of course, reflection led to overthinking. And anxiety. And panic. And anxiety. And more anxiety.

It shouldn't be like this.

Like anyone else, she had fears. But now they were taking over her mind. Like a nervous tic, she would impulsively read articles like:

How to Break It to Your Parents without Breaking Their Hearts

It's Not Me, It's Definitely You: Signs That You Two Aren't Meant to Be

30 People Share When They Knew and How Long It Took to Say It

How to Transform Your Kitchen into a Safe Haven: Mari Kondo-Style!

It was so stupid. She knew Kat was right.

On their last group chat, Kat tried to console her. "Just wait and see where it goes. You'll know the answer soon, but don't put so much pressure on it."

And maybe she was right. She couldn't deny she felt giddy during her Skype sessions with Michael. And she loved the memes and funny videos he sent her every day. But it was the lack of touch, of connection that made her doubt herself. She heard Nia fawn over her boyfriend when they first dated. But Nia was also in a hot mess of a relationship.

Their friend group could all see she was going to get married to him, but Nia and her boyfriend gave each other grief on the smallest things. "Can we talk about the fact men have a habit of purposely placing everything in the wrong place and ask us where it is? I swear I'm going to kill this man."

Leilani tried to give herself a break. But after dating for months and entering quarantine, it felt like she should know. Especially as every date seemed to bring him closer to saying it.

Maybe that was why she was rushing it.

She knew exactly how he felt. His touch, his attentiveness, and his childlike curiosity made it easy for her to be open with him. And though she hadn't confessed her concerns yet, she had hope he wouldn't judge her. He had such a strong, unshakeable sense of self that let him be who he was freely, that seemed to let him be sympathetic to anyone. It was hard not to want to be surrounded by a person like that. She felt engulfed by all the love he gave... but she feared she would drown in it, alone.

It was times like these that made it hard to join him on Skype. Because he was so happy, so confident in his own skin, never wondering who he should or should not be—she wanted to be like him: honest.

"You'd think they'd finally let up on the workload, but I feel like I go from my bed and crawl to the couch to work for twelve hours straight on a good day. I need to get off this project. Fuck COVID." Michael looked exhausted as he recounted his daily routine. And still, he was smiling at her.

"I could only imagine—I've seen the fishbowl consultant memes and they don't exactly push me to pursue a career at a Big Four. Have you heard of any other projects starting soon? Maybe you can start backfilling your current role while you look?" She kept staring at her video feed as she said it. Having the ability to look at herself while talking made it tempting to constantly fiddle with her hair to weigh down some of her curls.

"I'm looking, but they all sound just as frustrating, which is bad. Usually, they wait to staff you on the project before letting you know how bad the work is."

"Jeez, that bad?"

"I mean, so many of our clients are flipping out, trying to force their old systems to work in a digital era despite the fact none of it will allow for their people to work and operate. They want a job that requires at least a few months to be done in less than a week with a small team of recent college grads, a consultant who will QA, and a manager who will 'yes, sir' them. It's fucking nuts. They're all nuts! "

"My god. I swear, I hate corporate America."

"Leilani, you work in corporate America."

"Exactly. I'm—sorry. My little sister is calling, give me a second."

Of all people, she didn't expect an incoming call from Zoë. Ever. The handful of times she ever got a call or text from her was when…

She went on mute and tried to hide any damning facial expressions from Michael.

"Zoë—what's wrong?"

"It's Dad—we don't know yet. When can you fly back home?"

BELEN, LONDON— MARCH 2020

Belen couldn't help but think of that scene in *Love Actually*, when they start the movie with shots of Heathrow Airport and the British narrator begins his speech about how depressing news in the world drives him to think of the arrivals gate. The gushy scene of people hugging each other and reuniting with their family members provided the perfect illustration to the narrator's point: even though the state of the world likes us to believe we are filled with hate and greed, there is love all around us.

In that first scene, the narrator ironically talks us through the 9/11 terrorist attacks in the United States pinned up with a beautiful message: people dialing to their loved ones when they were about to die were, in fact, showing love, not hatred. Where again, the British narrator—unaware of how odd that comment was—sincerely reminds us love is *actually* all around.

As Belen sat on the floor of Heathrow Airport's gate, she suspected there wasn't going to be much love to go around.

She looked around at everyone, trying to argue their way onto a seat or desperately calling their loved ones.

She couldn't blame them. She was in the furthest edge of the gate entrance without bumping into the congested waiting room.

Despite her cynicism, Belen hoped Hugh Grant's voice would carry her through her destination. That, perhaps, she would feel less afraid, less wary of standing too close to anyone, less adrenaline bubbling up, and her heart would go from her ears and back to her chest when she walked through the arrivals gate.

She felt on edge. She was glad to have taken photos of her clean, empty apartment. But had she locked the front door? Turned off the oven? The voice of reason in her head told her yes, she had, but how could she listen to reason at a time like this?

It was roughly 8:30 a.m. but no one around her looked well-rested—including herself. Thankfully, her late night with Ginny gave her enough time after the President's travel ban to book a flight within minutes. It wiped her entire bank account clean, but at least she was one of the few who was going to make it home before it was too late. She already saw a flurry of texts from her friends abroad who weren't able to get flights. She felt guilty for complaining, knowing she could have easily been in their shoes. She sighed at the thought and reached for her hand sanitizer again.

Policy-wise, beaconing people to return home felt right. This wasn't a domestic problem, and though difficult, she knew everyone needed to hunker down. But knowing and accepting were two different things. Deep down, Belen recognized the English NHS would provide top-tier health coverage through her student insurance. But it left the question of whether she could manage to stay financially stable abroad while her family faced it alone in Los Angeles. Her instinct to return home made it clear: she needed to be there to take care of them. Her mind kept drifting to alternate solutions to allow her a moment longer at her university, a second longer to salvage an impossible situation.

Pero el hubiera no existe.[9]

She kept her eye on the gate while she waited for her mom to pick up the phone. It was late, but she had promised her to call once she reached her gate.

"Mami?"

Her mother's voice sounded worn. "Belen. How are you, mi niña?"[10]

"Um, okay. I think I have everything. And my friend promised to send me anything that didn't fit in the luggage."

"Have you eaten yet?" Belen was lucky the airport speakers sounded right as her stomach grumbled. She was a little early for her flight but hadn't eaten since 7:00 p.m. the night before. Nor had she slept.

"Yeah, I had a sweet bread and coffee."

"Make sure to eat fruit too. I don't want you…" Sick. Right.

"I will. I'm okay, it looks like the flight will arrive on time. Around nine-thirty at night?"

"It'll be a long flight. You'll be exhausted. I'll make sure to have something warm for you. I'll pick you up at our spot."

"But stay in the car! Don't come in. I'll meet you at the entrance of the corridor."

---

9   Translation: "What if" doesn't exist
10   Translation: My girl (term of endearment)

Though she really didn't want her mom to go to the airport and potentially risk exposure, she knew she didn't have much of a choice. She would just have to run over to parking lot B and jump in the car.

She could hear her mom stifling a yawn through her words. "How much was the flight?"

"Oh, don't worry about that. It wasn't bad."

It wasn't. It was closer to abysmal. They say you can't pay for peace of mind, but she did: £2,437.

"Hmm, okay. And they haven't changed anything?"

"Not that I can see. I think they're getting ready to let people on the plane."

"May God protect you now and always. Te dejo para que te concentres. Te amo."[11]

"Amen. Sweet dreams, Mami. Primeramente Dios, te veo pronto."[12]

Shortly after she hung up, another intercom announcement signaled her flight to Los Angeles would begin boarding momentarily. The fear her flight would be cancelled was quickly replaced with the fear of being in a confined space with nearly a hundred people who could potentially have the virus.

She hoped it was love that was in the air.

Feeling her anxiety rising as she took her assigned seat, she tried to practice her breathing exercises before giving up and taking two drops of skullcap Maggie forced her to take with her abroad. Though it took some time for the medicinal herb to take full effect, by hour two, she had occupied her mind on a mental checklist:

---

11 Translation: I'll let you go so you're able to focus.
12 Translation: God willing, I'll see you soon.

1. *Call LSE for updates on my academic transcript.*
2. *Figure out if professors will record attendance or if I need to continue taking them live in a different time zone.*
3. *Confirm with UC San Diego my classes will give me college credit.*

And as she continued to plan when and how to work through her list, she stayed buckled, keeping her eyes closed, nodding herself to sleep.

She dreamed of an older man on an empty road with sad brown eyes, bloodied, holding his arms open and welcoming her. Though she wanted nothing more than to hug him, she knew she had to walk away, leaving him there. Alone.

***

It had taken her a few more hours than expected to get up.

Six hours, in fact. It was 2:00 p.m. and she felt she had lost an entire day to communicate with her London School of Economics coordinator and email her dean to verify her credits. Though she felt better after eating and sleeping in her own bed, she felt groggy—angry and frustrated she had to be home at all.

But hearing her mother trying to quietly open the door made her smother that feeling. She couldn't give herself the space to air her grievances. Not yet, anyway. So she pretended to still be asleep but inadvertently fell asleep again, lulled by the smell of her mother's strong VS Rapture perfume and the softness of the sheets.

The next few days followed the same rhythm. In waves of disorientation, she kept her body on a London schedule to continue her classes in a sad attempt to retain some connection with the professors who would determine her acceptance into graduate school.

But graduate school was too painful to think of for too long. She took it a step at a time.

For all her skepticism and chronic criticism against the US government, she knew the lockdown would only be for a few weeks. The medical world didn't fall apart just because of poor leadership. It was built to withstand time.

So she doubled down on her efforts to stay on track: she studied, applied for internships, and prepared for LSE application while at home. She helped her mother in the mornings by making breakfast and cleaning and helped Axel with his online classes. He was all too happy to be away from the students who mercilessly made fun of him and used the mute button all too often to cut off his bullies during Zoom calls.

Though she wished she could spend more time with her mom, Belen knew her mother felt better about going into work without worrying about the shaky Wi-Fi or if Axel was actually doing his online schoolwork.

Still, she wished she had more time to talk to her; she had vivid dreams of Axel and her mother arguing and wanted reassurance everything was okay. That everything would be okay.

Instead, Belen cherished the small moments with her mom before Axel woke up and her mother left for work. She took the time to connect with Axel by sharing a meal during his lunch time and her "would be dinner in London." She tried to adjust to the mid-afternoon bedtime by soaking in the sun streaming out of her window as she nodded off. And she optimistically looked forward to having the entire house to herself as she woke up just past midnight for her first classes and had the rest of the night to apply for internships.

The schedule distanced her from the chaos in the news. She couldn't bear dealing with much more than what was discussed in class and spent most of the night half-listening to her shows on Hulu. In some ways, the isolation felt like a layer of protection. Even when she connected with her classmates in the UK, she felt removed from everything happening. They tried to reassure her she could watch the recording of the necessary lectures at her own pace, but she wouldn't let herself. She wanted to prove to her professors, to her deans, and to herself she could do this. Pandemic or not, she would succeed.

Even when Maggie commented on Belen's weight loss and pale complexion, Belen shrugged it off. She was getting things done. And helping her mother and brother. Her stimulus check finally hit her account. Everything was as fine as it could be.

It wasn't until Belen saw her mother's stimulus check and the notice about their VA-backed loan arriving together she noticed something was off.

She opened the letter and learned her mother's forbearance plan was approved for a six-month grace period. Belen held off on talking to her about it until she came home later that day. Her mother must have known this was coming. Belen was still awake at 5:00 p.m. and sat at the dinner table.

"Todavía no te vas a dormir?[13] It's late, Belen. Well, for you."

Her mother hung her keys near the door and changed into her house slippers. Belen held the letter from the bank.

"I want to talk to you about something." The exhausted look on her mother's face made Belen hesitate.

"I'm sorry, Mami. Do you want me to first serve you a bowl? We still have caldo de res[14] from yesterday."

---

13 Translation: You're still not asleep?
14 Translation: Beef Stew

Her mom shook her head and reached for a water bottle from the fridge before sitting next to her at the table.

"You sound serious. What do you want to talk about? Is it school?"

Belen began to unfold the letter and laid it in front of them. "School is fine. Don't worry. But Mami, what's going on? I just got this notice."

Her mother looked around the room and whispered. "Where is Axel?"

Belen kept her volume at a normal level. "He's watching a musical in his room. He finished his homework early."

Her mother nodded once before focusing her attention again on the letter. "Don't worry about the letter. But don't mention this in front of him. He's going through so many changes I don't want him to worry."

"Pero Mamá, this is serious. It's not nothing. When did this happen? When did you plan to tell me?"

"Lower your voice!" Her mother paused, lifting an ear to ensure Axel wasn't nearby.

She sighed and looked at Belen. "I don't have to tell you. I'm the mother, not you. And I'm handling it. Okay?"

"I know that, but... can you at least tell me what happened? Maybe I've heard of alternate solutions—"

"I'm working with the VA to get this managed. I speak to the specialist every week, and we figure out a plan until I get a new job—"

"New job? As in, there isn't one now, or you're taking another?" Belen felt her stomach burn and thought eating that last avocado may not have been the best idea...

Her mother looked like she was near tears but kept each one securely guarded, unwilling to let one fall. Her mother put her elbows on the table and let her hands cradle her chin, covering her mouth as if to not let any words out.

Belen remained quiet, her arms hugging her midsection.

Her mother sighed. "They have me furloughed. I have been looking every day to get this fixed. And if this interview goes well, we'll be okay for the next few weeks. It's hard to find a job that pays the bills, but luckily I have some savings that is getting us by."

"Maybe I can—"

"No."

"¡Pero, Mamá!"

"No, Belen. That's my final word. You're not going to take a job. We can't both expose your brother to the virus. And you need to focus on your studies. I don't want to hear excuses of why you couldn't finish your degree. You're almost there. I'm not letting you throw your education away."

Her mother moved away from the table, unwilling to look at Belen.

"Mami—"

Her mother's stare finished her sentence. Belen looked at the stimulus check and considered her options. Her mother had left the dining room to the kitchen, ready to pour herself some stew.

"At least let me give you my stimulus check."

"Belen, ¿eres sorda o qué?[15] I said no!"

"I'm not taking a job! I have things covered for school through the end of the semester and expect a partial refund for the part of study abroad program. Let me help. I can't study if we don't have a roof over our head! I know you have this, but let me help. Just think of it as a loan. Please."

---

15   Translation: Are you deaf?

Belen gripped the stimulus check. "Mamá, don't let your stubbornness impede help. I'm home. You will know if I need anything."

Her mom pursued her lips and slightly shook her head. She stared at Belen, contemplating and weighing the options. Eventually she let out a breath.

"It's a loan."

Belen smiled and hugged her. "I know."

Belen would never ask for the money back, but she knew her mother wouldn't accept it otherwise. She hugged her mother tighter before finally serving herself some food. She gathered all of the documents and hid them in her mother's room.

But Belen's thoughts raced. She knew of friends who tutored kids in Spanish for a decent pay. She knew she could finesse a good amount of money by guaranteeing they would receive at least a merit in their program if they hired her. And she had always been great at writing. Offering to review American college applications could help gather a few more dollars. That at least could help collect an extra month or two of rent money. They were behind, but she could fix it.

One step at a time.

OLIVIA, SCOTTSDALE— APRIL 2020

———

Olivia felt the drinks hit her on the way back from the bar but managed to mostly sober up the car ride over. The night was pretty uneventful, with Cadet Caleb turning out to be a disappointing kisser and Morgan throwing up her eighth shot of tequila. Paige looked unfazed and laughed at how much of a wreck Morgan looked like (and probably felt like). As Paige kept making jokes about Morgan as she drove, Olivia laughed when it was appropriate and let her mind wander to a hot bath that would get her out of her sweaty dress and sticky heels.

After being dropped off at her apartment complex, Olivia made her way to her floor, noticing how quiet the elevators were for a Saturday night. Even on social media, people weren't really sharing many travel photos. It seemed as if most of the world had gone to sleep while she danced the night away. She had uploaded great shots of the night on her story, but hesitated to post a particularly great shot of her outfit and weight loss at the risk of rocking the social media boat. She continued to stare at the picture until it melted into another disappointment and focused on quietly entering her apartment.

She figured she would be met with a quiet apartment but was surprised to see Priscila still awake at 2:00 a.m., under blankets, eating ice cream, and watching some crime thriller movie with Brad Pitt. Her inky black hair was still in intricate braids, but they looked a bit loosened and frizzy. Priscila turned to look at her as Olivia moved into the room and gently closed the door. Olivia was hoping Priscila would mostly ignore her disheveled appearance and let her gracefully bow into her room.

"Hey."

Damn.

"Hey, Priscila. What are you watching?"

"*Seven*. How was your night?"

Olivia winced at the comment. Priscila leaned back onto the back of the couch and was still looking at her.

"Not bad. I was with Morgan and Paige—you remember them, right?"

"The tiny blonde sorority chicks we met at Porters?"

Olivia peeled her high heels off, unable to walk further into the apartment with shoes that clung to the floor with an alcohol-infused-adhesiveness.

"Yup, the same ones." Olivia held her heels as she moved to sit on the corner of the couch. She went on:

"They're super sweet. You'll need to come out with us sometime. They send their hellos. But yeah, we went to Tucson, and they loved it. Can you believe they've never been there? They were so surprised to see some of the bars you took me to. I swear, there are parts of Tucson that remind me of New York City—I mean, even my followers thought

I was there until they saw the geo tag. Tucson needs a good PR team, because it's a dream. Thank god for me. Even Paige was saying she was going to go back and do a photo shoot in Valley of the Moon next—"

Priscila tilted her head and her smile tensed. "You guys went to Valley of the Moon? The fantasy park I told you about—"

Olivia interrupted, confused at her behavior. "Yeah... that one. I didn't realize it would be a problem—"

Priscila shook her head. "It's not! I just... when I mentioned it, I just meant it was a special place my uncle used to take me to, so... Anyway, did you guys enjoy it?"

Olivia nodded but looked down to rub her feet. Olivia couldn't help but feel bothered by Priscila's tone. It was a public area. She didn't understand why it was such a big deal for her to go there. But not wanting to cause a fight, she tried to brush it off.

Priscila's smile straightened more before she turned to look at the television. It was clear it was bothering her, but Olivia didn't bother addressing it. If Priscila couldn't speak up, Olivia wasn't going to bother. But she also didn't want to feel more uncomfortable in the apartment.

"Oh, by the way, I showed some of your photography to my manager. She agrees if you're ever open to it, we'd love to have you as a photographer."

Priscila looked a bit surprised but thanked her anyway. "I mean, when this virus thing is over, I wouldn't mind doing it."

Like clockwork, Priscila never failed to bring up the damn virus.

Olivia couldn't help feeling annoyed. She was trying to make a friendship happen, but Priscila always had something negative to say. It hadn't taken long to see Priscila was a pessimistic person, but the virus had inflated so much negativity into their apartment it felt like Olivia could pop any day. She still didn't know Priscila very well, but it was getting more difficult to avoid the topic about the virus with the child of a doctor.

Olivia sighed. It seemed to her Priscila didn't understand business, so Olivia chose her words precisely. "Look, how bad could it be if the governor is keeping so many businesses open? I think we need to trust these elected officials a bit more—they're doing what's best for the economy. Closing everything down isn't going to help fight the virus if there's no income coming in."

Priscila crossed her arms as she leaned back before laying into Olivia:

"Right... because the current administration has invoked such a strong vote of confidence? Look, I am the first to point out this closure is impacting business. *I fucking know.* I just got laid off yesterday and I'm seeing my dad struggle to secure funding for the clinic because all of the investors and businesses that usually donate are afraid of being forced to temporarily close. I'll be the first to call this situation shitty, especially if the restrictions happen and they last for months on end. *I know Olivia.* I'm not a fucking moron."

Priscila seemed calm, but her voice was full of sarcasm. Olivia wasn't able to get a word in before Priscila continued.

"This virus isn't a seasonal flu. People are dying, and we know nothing of it. My dad and brother are on the front lines trying to protect us. My dad is retired and was helping out in the clinic as a volunteer—he shouldn't be risking his life because the governor, this administration, or businesses are too greedy to protect their citizens first."

Olivia felt heat rise to her cheeks.

"If your dad wants to retire, he can retire. No one is asking him to come out of retirement to help out. Your dad is doing a great thing, it's true. But this virus is being popularized to tarnish the nation. It's being weaponized. This isn't going to kill young people. Most of the cases so far are in Washington and California, and it's just old people being affected. This virus isn't hurting anyone who wasn't already going to die."

A large smile appeared on Priscila's face. "Great to hear that. It's that mindset that landed us here. Do you want to tell that to my brother who was beat up because some xenophobic asshole blamed him for bringing the 'Chinese flu?' Do you know how much shit he's gotten for being part Chinese? He was in his scrubs when the hospital staff found him beat up in the parking lot. He has to take a fucking medical leave and stay with my parents for his protection. And not a goddamn person is helping bring those perpetrators to justice. This virus is causing hell—and it goes beyond the people infected. It's not just a medical issue. It's a societal problem, and we have zero defenses. Sorry I don't want to go out with your friends just because I'm bored. I recognize there's a need to stay home."

Olivia was surprised—she didn't know Priscila was Asian; she swore she heard her speak Spanish on the phone several times, but it did explain some of the Asian customs and decor she had noticed around the house.

Still, Olivia's grip on her shoes made her knuckles white, though she mustered an even tone.

"Look, I'm sorry to hear that. But what does it have to do with what's happening locally? It doesn't change the fact sheltering in place isn't going to help anyone. It's not me being bored, Priscila. I am alone here. Alone. I am aware I need to wash my hands, and I'll use hand sanitizer. But please try to see I just got here, just now making friends and potentially meeting someone, and it's not okay to ask me to say home twenty-four-seven."

Priscila took a deep breath. "I can't imagine being away from my family and friends right now. I'm sorry. I'm just really upset, and I took it out on you because… well, I don't feel comfortable being exposed."

Olivia took it as a positive sign to continue. "And I didn't know you lost your job. I am sorry about that. Can I do anything to help? Other than carrying Clorox wipes everywhere."

Priscila scrunched her face and slowly shook her head. She leaned back and covered her face with her hands. Muffled, she finally responded.

"I'm fine. I'm working in IT for my dad's clinic while I figure it out. He's giving me an allowance, so I should be fine with rent and all. But it's just… fuck this virus. I really hope I'm overreacting, but it doesn't look likely. In any case, me fretting isn't going to fix it. I just need to focus on helping my dad with the clinic and making sure my brother doesn't drive himself crazy during his medical leave."

"Is he flying back, then?"

Priscila looked at the ceiling, letting her hands rest on her stomach.

"Yeah. Vincent decided to come home while he recovered. He's super frustrated they wouldn't let him continue to work in the hospital. The school encouraged him to take time to recover since his right wrist is pretty messed up. He's ambidextrous, but UDub insisted he went home. But honestly? They probably figured they couldn't protect him." She shook her head. "And even though he's fluent in Spanish, they know people wouldn't trust him because he looks Asian. It's so fucking frustrating, the internalized fear people have. Cheeto man doesn't help by fucking calling it the 'Chinese Virus.'"

Olivia burst into laughter. Priscila gave her a disheartened look, which caused her to laugh even harder. The more Olivia tried to stop, the more she laughed. Priscila's smile turned into a giggle, but her laughter quickly turned into tears.

Olivia watched as Priscila tried to smother her tears, defenseless and alone.

Olivia moved to hug Priscila. She promised to order her some pizza and have a full day of fun planned for the next day. Even as she held Priscila, Olivia knew things just had to work out for her. Her father was a notable doctor, and she was in a lucrative industry—a tech company was bound to need a computer scientist. And her brother... well, he would bounce back and could work at the clinic while his father kept an eye on him.

Priscila, as usual, stayed quiet for a while, letting Olivia shower her with encouragements it would be okay in the end. Olivia reassured Priscila life would be better: her aging parents were well off, her brother would have more guidance from her father, and she was donating time from her retirement to support an important organization.

Olivia hugged Priscila tighter for a moment. "This is nice. Not the things you're going through, but being able to do this. Sharing. I know you have your friends and your family in Tucson, but I'm glad you told me. I know it sucks to be away from them, but I am here for you too."

Priscila stayed quiet but let Olivia continue to hold her.

LEILANI, OAKLAND INTERNATIONAL AIRPORT—APRIL 2020

———

Of the two airport options, SFO had been the typical choice for her travel plans. Clean exits and entries, larger array of airlines, decent food, and it was simply built for yuppies. Oakland wasn't too shabby, and, because of its size, it was an easy travel destination. But the situation forced her to pick the fastest arrival time, and that meant traveling directly from Oakland to Hobby.

It wasn't like she was expecting the airport to be full. She was relieved it wasn't—it was just creepy. Other than the occasional custodian or flight staff member, she was alone. Hearing her own footsteps echo through the empty terminal gave her chills. She raised the volume of her headphones, trying to tune out the thumping from her chest.

At her gate, she started to download movies and shows to carry her over for the next few hours. She had to lower her audio to figure out how to board. Though she planned and timed her arrival to Hobby Airport, she was clueless on what the new procedures would look like. As boarding time approached, she saw two elderly people and three young adults approach the gate, fearful and intentionally spaced away from each other. When all six of them were boarded, the anxiety of her travel increased. The lack of open air, the time spent with a mask on, and being encapsulated in a nearly empty yet still occupied plane had her fingernails digging into her thighs. She tried to remain as balled into herself as possible, mustering the power to not touch anything else she didn't need to. She prayed to God she could make it through.

When rounds of turbulence hit and canceled their flight's drink service, she knew he had heard her.

Though Oakland had scared her, it didn't prepare her for Hobby. She knew the airport's layout from years of traveling, but the contrast to Oakland's airport made Leilani's heart rate increase. Late April always brought rain and tourists, but it left Leilani nervously scratching herself at the blatant disregard of a pandemic in her hometown.

Having lived in California for so long made her forget how stubborn Texans were.

She sighed in relief the moment she saw the truck drive up to the curb of the passenger pick-up spot.

Her sister's GMC was still a bit older, and the gray color made it look a bit more worn than it was, but it was still in good condition. As a teenager, Leilani was embarrassed to be seen driven in it. But now, it gave her comfort.

As Aisha came around the car to help her with her luggage and hug her, the familiarity of things that never change anchored her: her sister's "VS Rapture" perfume, the odd rumble of the GMC's engine, the telltale stain Makellah had borrowed the car yet again to grab a Whataburger Patty Melt.

She was home.

***

Sometimes she questioned her sanity. Why is it you only remember the past with a rosy lens until you're thrown back into it?

It didn't take long after she arrived for her to be driven insane. Even without Candice there, or maybe because Candice wasn't there, it was a mess. Her sister was the only one who could truly manage the household.

Aisha was grown and married, with kids of her own. But that meant she needed to bring the little ones with her as they helped around the house in preparation for their father's return.

Her father would be the first to claim he was fine, but Aisha gave her a brief update after Zoë's call explaining the situation. Yet again, her father was pushing his body past his limits and disregarded advice to seek medical attention after his boss, Josue, noted his shortness of breath and unstable position on a ladder. Josue was eventually forced to tell Aisha when it was clear they would all have to chip in to push him to go. Still, the unexpected hospitalization as a precaution sent the sisters in a frenzy, and Leilani gathered her things to stay at her father's for at least two weeks.

It also meant Leilani was forced to babysit. The amount of times Aisha's kids tried to steal her phone was a job in itself, and her annoyance with Zoë only grew. Technically, they were both supposed to take care of Eric, Asher, and Dani—but Zoë couldn't have cared less.

While Makellah and Aisha's husband finalized the paperwork and sat through their father's out-patient care instructions, Aisha took the lead of cooking food for all of them. Zoë was assigned cleaning responsibilities Leilani would have to do quality assurance on, knowing full well Zoë would likely drop most of the workload on her.

Leilani finally had the kids settled long enough to grab some water and check on Aisha.

"Hey, do you need any help?" Looking around the large kitchen island, she saw Aisha rubbing chicken pieces with marinade and transferring them to a tub.

"Hm? Oh, no. You're helping me out a lot with the kids. What time is Daddy getting here with Makellah?" Aisha continued to cycle through the process and occasionally checked on the chicken stew she had on the stove.

"Closer to six? She hasn't updated me, but I also can't find my phone."

Leilani glanced at the kitchen clock and noted they would arrive shortly.

"Eric! Give Auntie Lani her phone back!" Still in her groove, Aisha bellowed across the house.

Leilani flinched. "Are you sure they're going to hear—"

"I don't have it!" It turns out mothers have a capacity to yell at a tone that forces their children to hear their words from any distance.

"Don't give me lip—give it back!"

After some grunts and rustling, small footsteps approached the kitchen. Asher timidly stood at the doorframe, waiting to be granted permission in.

"Well?"

Asher walked over and pulled Leilani's phone out of his sweater.

"Sorry, Auntie. Here's your phone."

He handed her the phone while she ran her fingers through his curly 'fro. "Thank you, Asher. I might lend you my phone for a game or two if you behave." His brown eyes lit up before he ran out of the kitchen, nearly bumping into Aisha as she moved the tray of chicken into the oven.

"No running in the house!"

"Sorry, Mommy! Auntie Lani is lending me her phone because I gave it back to her!"

The sounds of a movie blasted at full volume drowned out the children's retorts.

"They're so cute, but wow, they have so much energy."

"I'd have that much energy too if I didn't have any responsibilities. Since you're not doing anything, lift this pot cover up for me."

A hum of a car engine and a door slamming open cut the conversation short; the kids ran toward the entry with Asher speed walking behind the others. Not much longer, Makellah's laughter rang through the house as she tried to pry the grandchildren off of their grandfather.

Makellah waltzed in with the keys swinging around her fingers. "Oooh, it smells good in here! 'Isha, whatcha making? Is it jerk chicken? I thought Dad couldn't have that, because of, y'know, the heart attack and all."

Sighing, Aisha continued to stir the pot. "He didn't have a heart attack. It's called stable angina—the doctor should have told you during the out-patient conversation. And that's why I'm baking it and making stew. Knowing him, he's not going to want just soup. You were supposed to pay attention, Makellah."

"Same shit. His heart is broken."

"Makellah!"

"Oh, you know it too. He's never been the same since mom left and it's finally catching up to him in old age."

Aisha tensed at the comment and turned her back to Makellah. Sensing the awkwardness, Leilani slowly moved toward the door.

Makellah changed the subject. "If we're having soup for dinner, I'm going to step out and eat before he gets in here."

The comment seemed to snap Aisha out of her anger, and she turned.

"Oh no, no, no. You are eating with the rest of us. And that reminds me—stop using my car and clean up the sauce stains on the dashboard and carpet. How are you missing your mouth? Are you squeezing the juice out of the food before eating it? You eat like a man."

Leilani took the opportunity to slowly inch her way out of the kitchen. "It'll be another hour before we eat. In the meantime, I'm going to check on the kiddos. Text me if you need me!"

It wasn't that they weren't allowed to talk about her mom; they just weren't allowed to side with her. Except Zoë. She made it clear she never wanted to be left with her father. She looked the most like their mom, and she was their mother's favorite. Her light brown skin and green eyes made her a beauty and when she straightened her hair; she looked like a tanned White kid. But the tight curls that ran down to her waist and the resting scowl were inherited from her father.

It's a wonder her mother didn't take Zoë when she left. Maybe it was too much to have her father's disdain painted on Zoë's face. In either case, they didn't speak of her around Aisha, Zoë, and their dad. They each had their own hatred for her mother, and it was easier to leave it alone than to start a war.

***

Though their father was getting up there in years, he still hustled around the house and herded his sheep like no other. He welcomed all of his daughters to his home, forced Aisha out of the kitchen, and even got Zoë to help set the table. Surrounded by his family, he hardly looked like he just stepped out of a hospital.

After saying grace, he ranted off on how the doctors were a hoax trying to squeeze them out of money. Throughout the dinner, Aisha and her husband exchanged looks and would nudge each other, having a full conversation no one understood but themselves. Leilani tried to pay attention, but sitting between Asher and Makellah, who picked at their vegetables as they discreetly tried to play a game underneath the table, made it difficult. She had to eventually ask Asher to give her back her phone to check on the battery when she received a text from Michael.

Hey, I hope you arrived okay. I know you're busy with family, but I'm praying that you all stay safe and hope to hear good news.

No sooner had she finished reading the text did she feel Makellah lean over and casually try to read her message. Leilani quickly locked her phone and sealed it between her legs. Aside from an eyebrow raise, dinner concluded with their father tiring himself from the rants and Makellah trying to lighten up the situation with her jokes.

After being relieved from her cleaning duties for the day, Leilani made yet another trip to the bathroom. Though she did need to use it, she needed some privacy. As she closed the door, she could hear Aisha comment to Zoë and Makellah, "That girl goes to the bathroom so much, she might fall in there. I always had to feed that girl bananas and milk because she was constantly constipated and wouldn't let us leave the bathroom until she had gone."

Turning on the sink, Leilani shook her head and looked at her phone. Going through her privacy settings, she changed all of the notifications to be hidden on the notification screen, used screen time to lock her social media and messages app, and hid pictures of Michael on her camera roll. She looked at Michael's contact and hesitated. After a moment of deliberation, she decided to add the nickname "Mickey" and added a "girls with bunny ears" emoticon to his name.

She had just sat down to use the toilet when Zoë barged into the bathroom. "Zoë! Get out! I need to use the restroom!"

"You've been in here forever. You don't live alone here. Get up!"

Forcing herself to empty her bladder as quickly as possible, Leilani zipped up and angrily washed her hands in the kitchen.

"Shit, we're out of milk. Ugh, why do bad things happen to good people?" Makellah lamented as she closed the fridge with her Oreos partially hidden under her arm.

Leilani leapt at the excuse to leave the house. "I could go pick some up."

"Thank you! Can you also pick me up some chips? Maybe some Hot Cheetos? Ooh, maybe some ginger ale too. You're the best, Lani! I'll pay you back!" With a kiss on the forehead, Makellah dashed off to their shared bedroom.

Knowing she wouldn't be paid back but grateful to be outside, she accepted the trade-off. She walked out of the house and immediately texted Michael.

We're good. He's good. Thank you for checking in. It's been nuts here! But anyway, how's your day going?

And before hitting send, she contemplated again, before adding one last sentence and finally sending the message.

I miss you.

***

It was finally cool enough Leilani could slip out the back-door. She walked along the grass instead of the park's pavement to avoid making noise, though it didn't matter. Her presence wouldn't be missed in a small house full of loud people.

South Park was right next to her house. She could take long walks in the long stretch of land while staying within a stone's throw of the house. Though she rarely enjoyed the park in its full glory during the day, she was grateful to have it to herself at dusk.

Once she was far enough from the house and occasional dog walker, she took her mask off. Though the fresh April breeze had brought her some relief, she hadn't grown accustomed to wearing a face mask and still constantly fussed with it. She already started to see some breakouts along her jawline and felt like she was reliving her eight years of awful acne all over again. It seemed being back home, eating rich foods, and running into the same people gave her an allergic reaction.

She never really felt comfortable in her own skin when she was home. Just thinking about it made her palms itchy.

But the growing dusk and lighted streetlights gave her relief. At 8:01 p.m., she FaceTimed Michael. She couldn't help but look at her reflection and fix a stray hair that wouldn't stay down as she waited for Michael to join.

Michael's bright smile appeared before the audio carried his hello.

Leilani returned his smile. "Hey, good looking."

Despite the initial fuzziness of the video connection, the stream cleared enough to show Michael was in his home office, trying to wrap up his workday.

"Hey yourself. How's your day going? How's your dad?"

"He's home and doing well. He's giving everyone grief for coddling him, and he's moving around all too much. He can't help it—he's never been pampered before."

"I'm glad he's home, and I'm sure he's happy all of his daughters are home."

"Most of his daughters—Candice couldn't get a flight out from New Orleans and hit delays. He'll slow down once she's home."

"Aw, I'm guessing she's the favorite."

He smiled and winked at her before going back to typing.

"Well, you're not wrong. She's the pride and joy of the household. I'm supposed to follow in her footsteps."

"By being a full-fledged lawyer in California?"

"Yup."

He closed his laptop and took her to his kitchen where he grabbed a slice of pizza he had in the oven.

"So I'm guessing you're never telling them you don't want to go to law school?"

"Exactly. That's the nice thing about working for a corporate law firm. I can work on the business side without ever mentioning I'm not getting my law degree. Dad wasn't super well informed on what Candice did to get her title, and she wouldn't rat me out. I'm all set!"

"You always have everything figured out, don't you?"

Leilani grinned and couldn't help but feel smug. "I even have your Christmas gift ready."

"My birthday is coming up before Christmas."

"I have that ready too."

"I can't wait for you to pick out Jo—"

"I have graduation gift options ready for her too—I haven't bought it yet, because I figured the least I could do was let you pick one out for her. I'm well aware she's getting her diploma next year."

"As crazy as you are for doing that, I'm grateful I don't have to deal with that. You're way too organized, but I love you for it."

She rolled her eyes despite feeling giddy. It was ridiculous, but she was worried he would hate this "quirk" and flip out on her. And yet…

"So you're doing alright? I know being around family can be difficult, especially nowadays. It can be…"

"Stressful?" She laughed. "It is. I've been here for a week, and as much as I miss them, I don't miss the complications that come with having a tight-knit family in a small house. Michael, imagine one bathroom for nine people. I'm going to lose it."

"Shit. Yeah, that's bad. And you're not used to having so many people in your space."

"Exactly. I want my own bed and not Makellah cuddling me at two in the morning. If someone is cuddling me, it better be you," she sighed. "I just miss home, my home... Anyway, how are you doing? Are 'Mr. and Ms. Smith' at the beginning or end of the movie?"

"Oh, they are most definitely at the end—my Cubs caps are falling off the wall from their... released aggression." He said with a smile. "I hate knowing how and when they like to get down... at least it's probably not going to be as dramatic as our next binge on Netflix."

"Oh god, I can't wait for next Friday. It's such a mess of a show. I am here for it."

"I don't think it'll be as great as 'Jessica-Thirty-Four' though."

"Oh god, I hate her. I don't think so either, but we're running low on material. As much as I love mind-boggling movies, I need bad TV to distract me."

"Leilani, did you ever peg me as a reality TV kind of guy? C'mon. We're all bored and miserable."

"Actually, I do think you've kept up with the Kar-Jenners."

"First of all, I have, and secondly, blame Joanna. She would watch the most random shit on TV, and I was an idiot and would watch it with her. She's actually the one who got me into *The Hangover* and *The Office*."

"Aw, you're totally a Jim."

"Then, that makes you my Pam. And I'm fully expecting a ton of voicemails while I'm in the annex of my apartment. I'm miserable here."

Leilani found a nice curb to sit down and adjusted her phone. There was no way she was going to record or listen to a message without her sisters finding out. It was too soon, too early. "I'll do you one better. How about I write you a bunch of cute notes I'll send you while I'm away?"

"Handwritten? Maybe we share them with each other at the end of the pandemic and treat them like love letters? Y'know, the way our grandparents probably flirted with each other."

Leilani smiled. "Sure. I have an empty notebook. Be prepared for some riveting journal entries!"

Though their conversation continued on into different subjects, she felt her excitement sink. Even as they eventually hung up three hours later and she snuck back into the house, she still couldn't figure it out. She kept reading and searching for advice on the internet as she used a double cleanser and moisturizer. She was completely engrossed in the article she almost dropped her toothbrush when Makellah spoke.

"Boy problems?" Makellah reached around her to grab her toothbrush and turn on the faucet.

"My god, Makellah. You scared the life out of me. And no—what you are talking about?"

"Really, Lani? I'm not stupid—and don't give me that look, you know I'm talking about being street smart. I know you have a boyfriend."

"Uh, no, I don't. And it's funny you think you know everything."

"Well, it's a boy problem. Or why you be searching through so many Refinery29 articles about relationships? You might as well have 'relationships' tattooed on your forehead."

"You really need to stop making things up. I went on a Google deep dive—you're telling me I'm the only one who gets stuck on random recommended pages late at night?"

"Right. So what did you initially search for?"

Leilani took advantage of the fact she needed to rinse her mouth to come up with a clean answer: "Screenplayed, *The Notebook*. They did a great analysis on romantic comedy screenwriting. I'll send you the link." Her hands began to itch again.

She heard Makellah mumble as Leilani left for the bedroom. Leilani wasn't convinced she had heard the end of it from her sister, and she decided to avoid additional interrogations by pretending to be asleep when Makellah stopped by their room and grabbed her headphones.

Once Makellah closed the door and left, she turned over and checked on Zoë, who, as per usual, ignored her existence. Under the covers, she returned to her phone and quickly found a YouTube video from Screenplayed in case Makellah asked more questions. Though her eyes felt tired and dry, she couldn't help herself from looking up more self-help articles:

How Do You Know If You're Settling? Pink Signs All People Ignore at the Start of a Relationship.

Twenty-Eight Signs He's the One

Are You Ready for a Relationship? We Asked the Experts, So You Didn't Have to.

When Do You Introduce Your s.o. to Your Family? We Asked Five Couples

Are Things Going Too Soon Too Fast? Thank COVID for Turbo-Driven Relationships.

Co-dependency or Commitment Ready: Which One Are You?

It was 2:30 a.m. and she still couldn't get her mind off her relationship. She was frozen in fear: what if her family never accepted Michael? As crazy as they drove her, she never planned to leave them behind, especially her dad and Candice. She imagined every scenario where her dad would reject him—and by virtue, her. Every article she found suggested the same thing:

> It's 2020—you need to stand with where your heart lies. Your family will eventually get over it, or they were never actually there for you in the first place.

Cute concept, she thought, but that didn't negate the pain that would come with losing a loved one or family. It didn't take away from all the great Christmas Days and birthday parties she shared with her family. Naturally, she should cut her losses and let Michael go. Even if she wasn't ready to.

But what if she had already waited too long she had no choice but to make a choice?

She had always dated behind her family's backs, and she always landed with duds. Her most recent ex, Daniel, was the closest she got to feeling love, and even then she felt like she was going along with it because... well, there was nothing wrong. He marked all of her boxes and probably her family's. There was no "but." She didn't realize having nothing wrong was also a problem.

She had waited for Daniel to end it despite having already mentally checked out six months prior.

She tried to remember how she had felt with Daniel but couldn't. Did she really have that much apathy at the end? Would it be this way with Michael? Or was she playing with fire by waiting a bit longer to figure it out? And still, she couldn't help but want to hold out.

She switched to her "hidden photos" folder for all the pictures of Michael, hoping one of them would give her a sign—or at least calm her down.

She stared at the most recent picture of them together, where they were dressed up in goofy Valentine's Day sweaters at China Live and thought of Michael's suggestion. She hadn't thought too hard about it, but it felt like writing to him might help her figure things out.

Checking that Zoë's mouth breathing was still even, she grasped in the dark for her work bag. Careful not to wake her, she used her phone's flashlight to grab her empty notebook.

It was an abandoned, branded notebook with the law firm's seal on the cover. She couldn't help but roll her eyes when they ordered one thousand dollars' worth of branded merchandise the clients would take and leave at an empty table.

But it would work.

Despite the paranoia of waking her sister, she grabbed her pen and began her exposé:

Dear Michael,

This is so damn cheesy, and I think you're ridiculous for suggesting this. Here, I am writing a letter to commemorate our first (and hopefully last) pandemic together.

OLIVIA, SCOTTSDALE— APRIL 2020

———

The screen went dark before the dialogue box appeared notifying her the meeting had ended for all attendees.

They say good things come in threes. She hoped bad things came in twos. Olivia was in an irritable mood and could have really used a boxing session to let it out... but that wasn't an available option for another fifteen days. Instead, she walked over to her meal-prepped eggplant casserole, ruminating on how much she hated she was still eating well without having anywhere to go to show off her weight loss progress.

She understood sales were down—it was bound to happen. She had not expected a 10 percent reduction in pay. That was a curveball. She preferred they fire people instead of handing out payroll reductions. She popped in her AirPods and considered drinking a glass or three of wine. She was disappointed it wasn't quite one o'clock in the afternoon and decided to hold out for a few more hours.

Even through her headphones, she could hear the clinking of dishes and some kind of noise emanating from Priscila's headphones. Olivia was able to navigate around her roommate despite Priscila twirling around the kitchen to retrieve eggs and pour them into a mixing bowl. Priscila seemed to not see Olivia and continued to bob her head to a quick tempo as she beat the eggs with a fork until she had a frothy mixture.

"Hey." Olivia attempted to start a conversation, but Priscila only nodded at her before continuing on her journey around the kitchen island. Even as Olivia reached for her food in the fridge, Priscila moved around her to reach for her carrots. She shut the fridge harder than intended, but Priscila was still bobbing along to her music.

Annoyed at being ignored, Olivia moved into the living room, watching Priscila from afar. Olivia had her music off and decided to try and enjoy the quiet of the day.

Until Priscila began to bang dishes.

Priscila must have really loved the song, because she began to beat the wooden stick onto the baking pan in rhythm with her swaying. She kept whispering in Spanish something about rumors and "*esquina*." Olivia's ten years of Spanish didn't help her make out much more other than "deer." *They are rumors, they are rumors, something on the corner? The deer?*

The song must have ended when Priscila stopped beating the cookware, but that stupid smile continued on her face. Olivia knew Priscila still hadn't found a new job, and the clinic had been receiving more patients. She couldn't think of what could be making her happy or why she was ignoring Olivia. The more she sat with those thoughts, the angrier Olivia got.

She was fucking alone. The least Priscila could do was pay attention to her a little.

She got a pay cut and the governor had just fucking extended the shelter-in-place for another fifteen fucking days. Olivia refused to use that damn mask to run in the Arizona sun. It was going to suffocate her. She was tired of being away from the few friends she had, and she wasn't able to post more about her Arizona travels—eventually, even the Cactus pictures got repetitive and annoying to her followers.

She tried to "date" guys through apps, but she hated small talk. Caleb from the bar must have gotten her handle from the girls. He had DM'd her on and off, but he had been particularly quiet the last few days.

And now her parents were calling her. Olivia quickly dropped her dirty dishes into the dishwasher and left the bubbly Priscila shoving baking pans into the oven.

Her parents hardly ever called, and if they did, it was always her mom. Her father was constantly busy with some portfolio or another. Even if he did have time for her, she didn't have much to say.

"Hi, Becca."

Olivia's mother responded with a sigh. It bothered her mother to be referred to by first name, and Olivia did so intentionally.

"Sweetheart, I've told you not to call me that. Why can't you—I hope you're okay."

Olivia moved from her desk to her bed. "If you mean 'are you a lesbian and homeless,' I'm not a lesbian, yes. I have a job and investing my employee shares as Richard told me to. And no, I'm not heading up to Upstate New York anytime soon."

"I'm glad."

Olivia hesitated. Even on Olivia's angriest of moments, her mother would dismiss her behavior and instead focus on how everyone's child was amazing in ways Olivia wasn't.

But not today.

"Okay, you're being weird. What's going on?"

Her mother stayed quiet for a moment. But Olivia noticed her slightly higher pitched voice come through the speaker.

"We're fine. I'm just letting you know your father and I needed to use some of the trust we had for you to cover some expenses…"

"Okay. For how long? I don't need it right now, but I want to make sure I have access to it if I need it." Especially with that salary cut. She still needed to source a new web designer to redesign her entire website and app to fit the new aesthetic.

"I wouldn't count on it for a bit."

"For how long though? Is this a short-term or long-term thing?" Olivia knew it had to be bad if her mother was this evasive.

"I don't know. Your father tied some of our assets to his financials in London, and things went… down. While Europe rebounds, we just need to stay put. Your father is confident things will come back up. So he's investing in tech stock with the trust to make up for the loss of value."

"Why doesn't he just put-up Grandma's house in Cambridge? Why use my trust? Dad could have used other properties Grandma left him."

"You know how your dad's side of the family is with those things. Your uncle is disputing the inheritance again, and while the lawyers are on it, your father doesn't want to use any of his English assets. You'll be fine. And if you need, we can purchase you a flight home."

"I can't go back!"

"Olivia Estelle, people are forgetting about it. That small incident is blowing over with the news of this virus. You're not that special."

Olivia could feel sweat collect underneath her tightly crossed legs. The idea of returning to New York made her feel like she'd break out in hives. It was too soon.

Her mother sighed. "Olivia, it's really not that bad. I don't know why you couldn't have just stayed at your Aunt Claire's for a month, and it would have blown over. Speaking of, did you speak to your cousin, Penelope? She looks amazing. I think she got a tan during her honeymoon with—what's his name? The lawyer's name is… my god, I can't remember it. Olivia, you have an incredible memory for these kinds of things—"

"Mom, hate to disappoint, but I have a meeting soon."

"Good luck in your next meeting, and don't forget to try that paleo diet Emily sent you, sweetie. Again, we'll rebound in no time."

"Okay. Will do."

She wanted to scream but instead she grabbed her phone and keys and got ready to leave. It was 2:00 p.m. and no one was going to schedule a call with her this late into the day or notice she was gone.

Olivia didn't care what he would think of her sending multiple texts within a twenty-four-hour period. She sent Caleb a DM.

It didn't take long for him to respond.

LEILANI, HOUSTON— APRIL 2020

———

Usually, getting woken up late at night would either throw her in a frenzy, make her lash out, or both. Unless there was an emergency, she didn't understand why anyone would interrupt the sacredness of sleep.

But when Makellah wakes you up, you don't question it. You wake up and get ready.

Leilani grabbed her phone and sneakers, though her eyes searched for her keys.

Between the late nights with Michael, Candice's absence, and her father's condition, Leilani was stressed. No amount of food or meditation could help her deal with her constant worry. And though she hid the Skype sessions with work excuses, she had nightmares of being found out. She was pretty sure the anxiety and menstrual syncing with her sisters had caused her cycle to go haywire and gave her stomach cramps like no other.

She needed a night out with Makellah. She needed this.

The dew on the grass was fresh and told her it wasn't even 3:00 a.m. yet. The May heat made it bearable to walk outside without a jacket. She followed Makellah into the gray GMC. They took off to the corner store and to Whataburger. They made a loop around to a Chinese chicken shop before parking back at the house.

They divvied up the food and enjoyed the soft hip-hop throwbacks from the radio station as they ate in silence.

"Alright, are you taking part of tonight's libations?" Makellah pulled out the six-packs of hard ciders and beers from the backseat. She rearranged the cupholders to fit a few drinks. Her pack of cigars laid at the center.

"I'll take a cider, but if you want to smoke, that's all you."

"Damn. I still can't get you to try it, can I? Y'know, I've gotten all but you and Candice to try it."

"I don't really like the taste."

Makellah threw back a mouthful of food and nearly choked as she laughed.

"You don't smoke because of the taste. Happy people don't smoke."

Leilani cocked her head and squinted her eyes.

"Aren't you happy? I'm happy. What are you implying?" Leilani continued to point with her uneaten french fry, unsure if she should feel insulted or stupid for not understanding Makellah's hidden commentary.

"Oh chickadee, you have much to learn. But fine, I'll take my friends with me later on."

Leilani finally let herself enjoy her fry and shook her head, ultimately dismissing Makellah's comment as nonsensical.

They continued to eat and drink for a few more moments before Leilani had to break the silence.

"When do you think Candice will get home? Why is she taking so long?"

"Candice will do whatever she thinks is right. There's no reason or form to her."

"She's literally a lawyer."

"I'm literally buzzed—what else do you want me to say?" Makellah usually was a lot better at these late-night runs. She taught Leilani how to shoot whiskey and keep her composure, how to drive, and more importantly, how to shop for a bra. For anything inappropriate, she was always the person she could count on. But she was off.

Maybe Leilani wasn't the only one stressed out about Candice.

Her phone went off again. It was the girls. They were commenting on something, and Nia had mentioned her. It was followed up by Kat and Brittany checking in if she was okay. She had been unintentionally unresponsive. With everything going on, she didn't know how to explain what was going on. Or if she should. They might be her best friends, but they also didn't understand her family life. Or even heard much of it. It just felt weird to approach the subject, and it felt easier to let it slide under the radar.

"Is it your boyfriend?"

Leilani felt heartburn, but it wasn't from the burger. But years of experience under these kinds of circumstances made her respond before she could even consider real transparency: "No, it's just my friends asking me how I'm doing. Ugh, they don't know about Dad, and I really don't want to get into it with them."

"Why not?"

Leilani shrugged. She was clearly getting rusty; pivoting away from Michael had forced her to enter more unpleasurable conversation topics. Leilani let the silence hang but Makellah wasn't as willing to leave it at that.

"Just tell them."

"Mhm."

"You're not going to. Are you?"

She gave her another uncommitted shrug. She knew they hated this: her unbothered attitude toward everything. But it was also why they liked her. She wouldn't really say anything, so she was the one person they could rant to. She sounded as if she was agreeing with them without ever saying so.

She bit into the remaining piece of the burger. The satisfaction she had earlier was gone.

***

It took a few more days for Candice to finally get home.

She never explained to anyone why she was so late. But her father didn't care: all of his girls were home. And it seemed his restlessness was amplified. He mobilized the entire house to clean and prepare for an outdoor barbecue, even if the recipes had to be modified due to doctor's orders.

It was odd Candice was late, but Leilani didn't care. She was just happy she was home. Candice was the only person who could really get the house in order. Even when Aisha lived at home, Candice would be the voice of reason, the one voice their father would really listen to, the one who demanded respect from the rest of the sisters.

Even Zoë sighed in relief when she saw Candice arrive.

As everyone lined up to greet her, Candice's light purple, sheath dress and matching shoes made her look almost like she didn't belong in the house. The subtle but expensive luggage was immediately placed in the closet's top shelf, high enough to avoid any accidents with the kids. But Candice's smile was gentle, and she had prepared gifts for everyone.

Soon after pleasantries, everyone gathered to the small patio and enjoyed the feast Aisha had prepared. Even Eric Sr., Aisha's husband, joined in the festivities of having the entire family together.

For the first time since quarantine started, Leilani truly felt at home. Like everything could be okay in the world. This virus wouldn't destroy this. This moment could last forever.

With Aisha passing out trays for seconds, Leilani allowed herself seconds and thirds. Even Makellah stared at her, probably impressed with how much she was able to pack in. Zoë seemed to have noticed this as well and made a comment when all of the sisters cleaned up after dinner. "I'm trying to remember what the food tasted like. I feel like I wasn't able to try anything."

Candice immediately eyed Zoë, but she either ignored it or didn't notice the attention. "Might as well have invited Kirby to the dinner table with the way Leilani was eating," Zoë continued.

"Zoë." Candice's one word struck as a warning, and Zoë didn't ignore it. Still, not one to keep her mouth shut, she let it go. "What? I'm just saying…"

"Say less then."

Trying to dispel some of the tension, Makellah tried to normalize the conversation.

"She misses Aisha's home-cooked meals and probably can't get this good Southern cooking in California. Can you blame her? Besides, we all stress eat, and we know the law firm has her working late nights, especially with the time difference and all."

"Speak for yourself, Makellah. I never stress eat. Actually, the only time I felt hunger was with Eric and Asher's pregnancy. They say boys make you stuff your face like no other, and they're not wrong. I was also super itchy, so I was constantly eating ice cream—anything cold made it go away." Aisha laughed and shook her head.

At that, Leilani held the dish she was washing.

"You get itchy when you're pregnant? What symptoms *didn't* you have? I swear having a child is like having a virus." Makellah kept wiping down the table, horrified at the woes of childbearing.

"Well, I knew I was pregnant the moment I had the itchy palms. There was this weird feeling of having to do something with my hands. And it was obsessing with just one food type before getting morning sickness and weird bowel movements."

"Ugh, ew. Can we not discuss that? We just ate." Zoë looked disgusted and tried to get Aisha to stop but to no avail.

Leilani didn't listen any further than that. Her mind kept replaying "pregnant" and "itchy palm." At the urge to scratch her palms, she fisted sudsy hands and tried to keep her panic at bay.

***

She continued to lie on her side at the edge of the bed and stared.

She had her phone in her hand and a note drafted. She felt... numb.

Hey, I don't know how, I'm on the pill and all. But somehow, I think I might be pregnant. I can't double check at home, but I've missed my period...

Her sisters had mostly left her alone after seeing she had stayed up for the last four nights and assumed she needed some time to sleep and recover from the work week.

Four nights. She had been a... mother? No, she knew better than anyone it took more than insemination to make a parent. Harvesting a... well, she wasn't a farmer either. She knew she could never make it as a lawyer—she always had a hard time giving a resolute answer or opinion.

But now, she had to.

Her arm was starting to fall asleep, but that didn't make her move. She felt static in her arm and still, she stared blankly to a wall.

There was a need to feel something. Anything to help her make a choice. To know what to do. Someone to talk to.

She wondered what her mother's last thoughts were before running away to her lover's arms without them. If she ever regretted her choice or missed them.

Wasn't abandoning them for dead just as bad as killing them? At least dying animals are put out of their misery.

She didn't dare touch her stomach. She couldn't. She didn't want to get attached. Or maybe, she was afraid she wouldn't be able to. She never had anything to care for like that. Others told her what to do, bathed her, cared for her, loved her. And in return, she did what was expected of her.

She scrolled through her photos until she landed on a picture of Aisha holding Dani. Dani was half asleep and Aisha looked confident and comfortable cradling her to sleep. She zoomed into Aisha's face and analyzed her soft gaze. Aisha held the world within her arms and her daughter let herself unfold there. There was a small pull in her heart that wanted that kind of love. She so desperately wanted to touch that love and hold it forever.

But her bank notification confirming her student payment was scheduled reminded her of her reality. She didn't need to open her account to know she had a balance of $217 to spend on food, credit card payments, and utilities.

It was selfish to bring someone into this world for unconditional love. Candice would never do that... right? There was no way to know.

No one could help her with this. No one would help her with this. No one should help her with this.

Michael... he could. And maybe would?

She tried to picture what he was doing. She had him on "Find My Friends" and knew he was home as of a few minutes ago. Was he binging on TV and trying to drown out his roommate's arguments? Would he be excited? Terrified? What if he... left?

She knew she needed to tell him. Even if she didn't want to, he had to know. She couldn't date him and not tell him. And maybe he would leave, and it would make it easier on her. Maybe.

Before she lost her nerve again, she copied her note and pasted in the text. Their last text ended oddly, and she knew he would want to talk on the phone. Especially with her skipping out on their last few nightly talks.

She sent it and ran out the door. Bile was coming up, and she tried to hide some of the noise with the sound of the shower and faucet running. She wouldn't be able to hide it from her sisters for much longer. But she would be damned if she didn't try.

She tried her hardest to prolong returning to her room until Zoë belted Leilani needed to get out and answer her texts that wouldn't stop buzzing.

She dressed, grabbed her phone and went out the back-door before anyone could question her. Her hair was already starting to dry with the summer heat when she plugged in her headphones and picked up the incoming call.

"Hey…"

"Hey…"

He looked flustered and couldn't get his mouth to quite close.

"You weren't answering my texts."

"I was in the restroom and didn't have my phone on me."

"Uh, right. Because of the nausea. So… first of all, I need you to know I support anything you do, but I do want to know what you want to do. I know it's not your body—sorry, it *is* your body, but it's not my choice—I mean it's not your choice. It is your choice and I'm not who matters here—"

If the circumstances were different, Leilani would have let it run on a bit longer. He rarely was so tongue-tied, and it would have been endearing to see him trip over his own words. But Leilani could only focus on one breath of air at a time.

Inhaling, exhaling.

"Michael. Thank you. I know what you mean."

He sighed and leaned into the video camera. He looked at her, waiting for some kind of answer. Any answer.

"I want to terminate it. I can't afford it. We can't afford it. Neither of us are ready to be parents, and I wouldn't pressure you into staying in a relationship because of a child."

"Hey, I understand, and I agree. What do you need me to do? I don't mean to be a prick when I say that. I just mean I want to help you, but you're miles away. Do you need me to make an appointment? Call Planned Parenthood? Drive you?"

Of all things, she didn't consider that. This unexpected pregnancy would ultimately send her away from her family. As she circled around the block and stood a few houses away from her father's home, she saw him coming out to clean his truck, his pride and joy. No sooner had he started to wipe down, his sisters trailed behind, trying to get him to sit still. He was still weak, but keeping him still required a team effort. Aisha looked eighteen again, ready to go back to her home and family. Candice wouldn't be able to take her calls from their father's cramped home. Makellah was due to run off—even during a pandemic, she would likely disappear and reappear at one of their sister's homes. Zoë might as well not live there with the amount of indifference she had toward everyone.

She heard of the Texas ordinance on abortions. She would need to go to Wichita, and even then she might not get an appointment. And there was no reasonable explanation for her disappearance if she were to go to Wichita.

She had to leave.

"Hey, Leilani. We don't need to talk about it right now. But you're not alone. I'm here with you."

Michael's voice helped loosen her grip on her phone and kept the tears at bay. She feared leaving, but she was more scared of bringing a child into a pandemic and her family's reaction.

Her heart moved again, but this time she felt it fall to the ground.

BELEN, LOS ANGELES— MAY 2020

———

Melatonin was her new best friend.

The week after her finals, she tried to readjust her sleep schedule. She knew she had to leverage what remained of May and couldn't sit around, empty-handed, watching as cases finally started to normalize. Most days, her mother joined her at the table as they both worked on job and internship forms and kept an eye on Axel who was perpetually muted by his teachers. Karma.

Transitioning back into society made her wish she could still hide behind the curtain of the night and ignore all of the news that only ever seemed to crawl out during the day. But seeing the bills flowing into their mailbox made her straighten her back and focus on looking at more internship postings at the kitchen table.

She enjoyed being with her mom as she worked and tried to make her laugh whenever she seemed to go… away, which happened more as of late. She knew the news had a way to bring her down and hated it was always playing softly in the background. But her mother insisted on keeping it on, occasionally staring off, hoping to hear some good news.

Despite the poor economic downturn, it seemed she was able to at least capture one job to support her through the summer. Having to fill the last of her onboarding documentation to "officially" start, Belen couldn't help but blast music—in part to keep the cheer of one success, and in the other to ignore the news.

Yet, her mind always sang the same song as hard as she tried to ignore it:

Michael Brown, Freddie Gray, Eric Garner. Pedro Villanueva, Melissa Ventura, Anthony Nuñez, Raúl Saavedra-Vargas, and Vinson Ramos. Botham Jean, Elijah McClain, and Philando Castile.

Jose "Jay" Soto. Daniel Prude. Carlos Ingram López. Breonna Taylor. Ahmaud Arbery. Daniel Hernandez. George—

"Breaking news: Videos of the protests from George Floyd's death…" She had to take off her headphones. She pushed away from the table to walk over to the television. Though censored, the video replayed the officers kneeling on Floyd's neck as the newscaster explained it continued on for eight minutes. The video cut away to the growing protests in Los Angeles. She switched off to another network for more coverage and accidentally navigated to the Spanish-language coverage.

The headline translated to: "Violent Looting in New York City." Coverage of the looting seem to overtake any reporting of the protest social media extensively covered. She switched to another Spanish-speaking channel with a similar headline. They were interviewing Latino business owners whose stores were vandalized or looted.

Her mother stood by her with contempt on her face but not much else. She eventually moved back to the table and continued to listen from afar.

Belen continued to stare—and with anger rising. Axel was already on the couch with his feet up and head down, playing with his phone.

"Did you know him?"

Belen snapped out of her fugue state, confused on who Axel was referring to. "Huh? Who?"

"Floyd? You've been staring at him, and I thought you knew him." He continued to play his game, not looking at her.

"I'm angry he was murdered, and I'm upset they aren't covering the protests. They're focusing on the looting more than they're focusing on the protestors."

Axel sat up and stared at the TV for a moment before responding. "It's boring to see people sit for a while."

She looked at him in disbelief, but… he was right.

Still feeling prickly, she sat back at the table and finished her supplemental information. Her job as a youth advocacy coordinator was surprisingly flexible with her inability to leave the house, and most of her work focused on activating young people on social media. It wasn't an internship on the Hilltop or in Sacramento, but she loved grassroots efforts and always looked forward to mentoring high school seniors during their college readiness program. They allowed her to start early as she finished the last bit of paperwork and introduced her to the team. She was already receiving messages from one of the students, Socorro, who was determined to go to a private college and was very invested in speaking with her.

Which reminded her…

"Axel, have you connected with your dean yet on the summer bridge program yet?"

"I don't have a dean." He was nearly yelling from his place on the couch.

"You know what I meant. High school counselor."

"I didn't know, and no, I haven't."

"Okay, put down your phone and message him."

"Or I could just do it from my phone."

"Or you could just do what I just asked."

"Why would I do that? I could do it from my phone."

Belen could feel her mother getting annoyed as she tried to focus on the job application form.

"Yes, but I'm telling you to do it from your computer."

"But you didn't say—"

"Why can't you listen to your sister? Axel, do as she says." Belen assumed her mother's tone of voice would stop her brother from arguing with her; Leslie de León didn't snap very often, and no one wanted to be on the receiving end.

Somehow, Axel was unfazed.

"I do listen to her. I was just listening to her. And now I'm listening to you."

"Give me your phone."

"No."

"Axel." Belen tried to implement the techniques she read in the books and pamphlets they gave her mother. "Give us your phone and email your counselor or you can sit in your room without your phone."

"I told you I'm not going to give you my phone."

"Axel, I'm giving you a choice—"

"Que 'choice' ni que nada. Dámelo."[16]

Her mom's chair screeched across the hardwood floor, and she moved to grab the phone as Axel resisted and pushed

---

16   Translation: None of this 'choice' talk. Give it to me.

her. He started to scream, startling Belen. She hadn't seen him behave that way in a long time.

Her mother hushed him. "Cállate—nadie de esta matando!"[17]

She was still trying to pry off his fingers from the phone, managing to restrain him securely and gently while he dug his nail into her hand. Even when he bit her, she didn't stop trying to get to the phone. When she finally slipped the phone from his fingers, Axel was released. He turned red and started to yell, "I can't breathe! I can't breathe!"

Leslie threw a deadpanned look at Belen she couldn't discern. Moving back to the table, her mother said, "And yet somehow you have a breath to yell."

He looked at them before storming off to his room.

"I don't know what they're teaching you in school but coddling him like you did there isn't helping him."

The door slammed soon after.

"Oh, because your performance did that much better?"

At her mother's pointed look, Belen dropped the subject and decided to focus on reviewing her loan repayment plan. And to no one's surprise, she would have never-ending debt into her forties. Though her spreadsheet tried to take into account the CARES Act, the scholarships Patrick had recommended to her last week, and potential repayment plans, graduate school seemed to sink her further into poverty instead of bringing her out of it.

She looked at the mortgage bill that laid not too far away from her mother and thought of the extra support Axel would need throughout high school. She looked at her loan

---

17 Translation: "Shut up—no one is killing you."

page and couldn't bring herself to continue recalibrating her spreadsheet.

She couldn't do it to them. Making them wait for her to pursue her dreams while they suffered through meager savings... It almost hurt her more by trying to make it work. She was tempted to just delete the whole file.

As she tried to, she accidentally clicked on Maggie's incoming text:

"Check it out: 'Ways to Pay for Graduate School.'"

LEILANI, EMERYVILLE— MAY 2020

———

It took all of her to not cry.

When she had finally managed to book and schedule her appointment, she was close to the ten-week cut off. In another world, she wouldn't have picked Planned Parenthood and would have taken a moment longer to pick something within network. But when she finally landed in California, it hit her she was running on borrowed time.

Not even California could save her from the changing terms on elective surgeries. She knew she had to bite the bullet and deal with extra two-thousand-dollar cost after the abortion. Right now, she just needed to get it done, and she was lucky enough as it was to have the option.

Sure enough, she had lost weight and felt increasingly tired as the days to her termination date approached. She was restless. But she was determined to not let her fear of doctors make her lose her resolve.

She told Michael she didn't want him to accompany her— knowing she had to carry his emotional baggage with her.

Even though he tried not to show it, Leilani felt he had some kind of reservation with the decision. But her mind didn't take a moment to contemplate his reluctancy as she focused on billing and he insisted on paying half of the copay and renting a car to drive her.

She knew he needed to be there. To be with her.

In the end, she was grateful he was. Most of the waiting was in the car before they brought her in. Though the pills were easy in theory, and they had explained when to take the subsequent pills, she wasn't prepared for her mental state. She still felt pregnant and nervous, but Michael held her hand, letting the tail of his wooden rosary bracelet briefly touch her.

It took all of her to quiet her sobs.

The number of times she ran to throw up, bleed through her sanitary pads and sheets, and balled in pain that first day embarrassed her. She felt her body fight her, and she felt betrayed by it. Even when she told him she didn't want him to take care of her, Michael gave her physical space before ignoring her requests and bringing her tea and a heating pad.

For the first time since they started dating, Michael hadn't opened his laptop once. Instead, he tried to massage her lower back and hold her when she felt the pain.

She gave in.

Though her body ached and the bleeding eventually normalized and her follow-up confirmed everything went well, Leilani could still feel the pain.

Fighting with her body that day made her realize something was wrong.

No, she didn't have regrets about the abortion. But she realized something was missing. She had an emptiness she didn't realize needed to be filled. She couldn't ignore it.

***

It didn't matter how many times she would move her body to a new semi-comfortable position; her body told her she was going to have to get up before her alarm went off. She pressed her eyes together more tightly and imagined the extra seconds of sleep were helping her rest more.

She never had the best imagination.

Rushing to the toilet, she rubbed her lower abdomen and wished she didn't live alone. If she was being honest, she wished she was living with Michael. The level of care he had given her was incredible. Despite wanting to be alone and ignoring him for the majority of the days leading up to *it*, she couldn't have done it without him. She wanted him to stay with her, but he still had a client who required him to come into the office at least once a week. He had to go before his manager berated him, again.

When she felt strong enough, she gathered herself up and turned on the kettle. As she waited for the water to boil, she went into her linen closet and grabbed the rice baggie Aisha made for her. The tea and lavender scented baggie eventually eased her pain.

She slowly walked her way back to the bed, unaware of the sunlight dripping from behind the blackout curtains. Taking one last sip of tea, she tried to nap off some of the pain.

Thirty-nine seconds later, her alarm went off. And as much as she wished she could mess around and pretend to do work while she was online, she knew she had to complete those RFPs, though she contemplated, like every day, if she truly still had to work. Her answer always came down to two things: (one) sadly, she was ambitious; and (two) she had to pay rent.

She started to get ready, albeit slowly. She rummaged through her drawers for her period panties and a heavy flow pad she reserved for Makellah's impromptu visits. Even with a hot shower, the intensity of the stomach cramps grew and reminded her of all the reasons why she even took birth control in the first place.

Though woozy, she reviewed the RFP that should have been completed by a partner last week but landed on top of her list of duties for today. Her clock didn't reassure her.

Unless she submitted by 8:30 a.m., Macey Dupré would email her at 8:59 a.m. ("Happy Hump Day! Hope this email finds you well..."), ping her at 9:01 a.m. ("Hey! :) Just emailed you. When is the RFP ready?) and call her at 9:05 a.m. ("Hi! How are you? Oh my god, I hope you had an *excellent* weekend..."). She dreaded being asked how her weekend was and knew she had to hustle.

After narrowly avoiding a game of pleasantries ("As per my last email, I mentioned the need..."), she made mindless website design edits and messaged her coworkers and Michael. Reading the memes, scrolling through the gifs, and seeing the videos of animals falling down made the stomach cramps hurt a little less. The laughing masked much of the uncomfortableness of her body.

But in the back of her mind, she knew what 11:00 a.m. meant. And the insistent need to check the time didn't calm her nerves. Every minute closer made her feel less giggly and more like a joke. It was like everyone was going to reveal her abortion in front of the client, the partner, her supervisor, and her coworkers, and she was being suckered into a call for it to happen. Though she knew the partners were fairly progressive—the firm was founded in Haight-Ashbury after all—the clients were not.

At 10:52 a.m., she prepared her fourth cup of tea. She calculated the time to sneak in and avoid the fluffy banter that was sure to ensue. At 11:02 a.m., she joined at the height of the "Chrissy Teigen and Alison Roman feud" her coworkers couldn't stop talking about. Without bothering to turn on her mic, Leilani sipped on her tea and gathered the feud between the celebrity chefs had brought her coworkers to decide on which team they were on. However, as soon as the partner joined the call, quick salutations led to discussions about the incoming surge in cases. Since Leilani was the lead paralegal, she multi-tasked through the hour-long call. She continued to make edits to a scheduling excel sheet and didn't notice how the end of the conversation had derailed into weekend plans, especially with the impending Memorial Day weekend.

"Oh right, Leilani, I'm sorry, I forgot to ask how your weekend went. You were off for half a week, right?"

Startled, she quickly unmuted herself and thanked her lucky stars it wasn't a video conferencing call.

"Ah, actually just two days. Ran a few errands. Not very interesting."

But of course, Jessica Hartley, the client liaison, lacked social awareness at Leilani's dismissive tone and kept asking questions before others could jump in.

"Oh, did you do anything relaxing at least?"

Leilani's vague and lukewarm responses satiated Jessica enough to finish the call with action items. Or so Leilani thought until she saw Jessica's ping:

"Are you ok? You sound unwell…"

She decided to respond with some truth:

> "Yes—just cramping; period coming soon :/ thank you for checking though!"

She didn't know what to do. Her heart was beating in her chest, and she worried how her heart was dealing with the stress. Unable to spur herself into working a bit more before taking a lunch break, she grabbed her mask, keys, and phone. As she ran down the stairs to walk over to the Peet's coffee a few streets away, she noticed the large Amazon box outside of her door.

She figured it must have been her four mason jars, but it looked a bit wasteful, and the box looked used with no shipping label. She couldn't help herself and opened it with her keys.

Inside laid twelve roses surrounded by chocolates and tea bags. There were sticky notes inside an envelope with Michael's handwriting as well as a can of chicken noodle soup and crackers.

When she saw what was inside, she teared up, sent a message, and went back to her apartment with the box. Her hormones might be in overdrive but the level of detail within the contents made the moment feel like it was worthy to write in the journal.

Dear Michael,

How do I even write this? Thank you. I could not ask for a better partner.

JULY 10
Hong Kong shut down schools amid a third wave.

JULY 7

AUG. 3
Trump addressed the death toll: 'It is what it is.'

JULY 1
Iran announced new lockdown measures.

Brazil's president tested positive.

JUNE 6
Coronavirus tore into regions previously spared.
The number of known cases across the globe grew faster than ever, with more than 100,000 new infections a day.

AUG. 1
The U.S. saw July cases more than double the total of any other month.

JULY 21

JULY 15

Tokyo raised its pandemic alert level.

Summer 2020

Big Talk From Big Tech On Racial Equity, But Not All Workers Are Buying It

study in South Korea found that older children spread the virus comparably to adults.

Total US Confirmed COVID-19 Cases on June 20th, 2020: 2,268,034
Death Count on June 20th, 2020: 119,717

JULY 10
U.S. set seven records in 11 days.
On July 10, the United States reached 68,000 new cases for the first time, setting a single-day record for the seventh time in 11 days.

JUNE 30
The E.U. said it would reopen borders.

AUG. 22
Global virus deaths surpassed 800,000.

JUNE 11

Coronavirus cases in Africa topped 200,000

JULY 17
India reached a million coronavirus cases, and lockdowns were reimposed.

AUG. 11
The Big Ten and Pac-12 announced they would not play football in the fall.

European leaders agreed on a $857 billion stimulus package.

LEILANI, EMERYVILLE— JUNE 2020

———

She was in her favorite sundress, a rich mocha color that complemented her brown skin, and her boyfriend was in his Sunday best, a crisp white shirt and khaki shorts. Leilani's face remained expressionless through Michael's hyperactivity that led him to sing about the joy of pizza. There was something uniquely contradictory to their personalities that always balanced each other out. Or drove each other away—it all depended on the day.

The sun warmed the concrete streets, letting the heat rise to the soles of their shoes and pushing the couple to reach home quickly. Leilani's apartment was tucked away in a bubble away from the protests, surrounded by empty streets and the occasional masked dog walker. The Amtrak train tracks and the polished tree line made her feel like she was surrounded by suburbia, undisturbed by the world around her.

But passersby's looking at their phone would miss the spray-painted "Black Lives Matter" concrete near the shopping malls. A tourist would run to join the spaced queue for the massive sale in the outdoor mall and perhaps only glance at the poster calling to join the protest the following weekend. Just as Leilani and Michael had ignored the exiting neighbors' BLM-printed face mask as they walked into the main hall of the apartment.

But they shared a knowing smile when they walked pass "Queen E" in her highlighter yellow hat, a more muted color than they were used to. They knew they'd go to Hell for this, but they couldn't help and snicker when they would see the elderly lady scurry off in a bright colored hat and a magician's cane, looking like a Bay Area Queen Elizabeth. Hence, her name. They couldn't figure her race and threw out guesses. ("Maybe she's an Afro Latina like Nia or a light skinned Black woman.") It added to the fascination with this flamboyant woman.

They held onto the small joy as they took off their face masks, washed their hands to Michael's approval, and finally served their pizza slices.

They had begun to eat when Michael received the first of two alerts letting him know dangerous activity could occur in his area and he needed to be vigilant of riots nearby.

"What the fuck is wrong with them?"

Leilani looked up from taking a bite of pizza. She looked over Michael's shoulder to see his phone. The second message reminded employees to take proper precautions to avoid the "incidents."

Leilani pulled away when she sensed him getting up to pace out his frustration.

"They're not even riots! Most of yesterday was peaceful gatherings in solidarity for Juneteenth. Why do they keep twisting it into something it's not?"

Leilani sat on the couch, tucking her legs under her and underneath the couch pillows, watching him pace. He continued on:

"It's just ridiculous how complicit my company is in this. Even the language they use in the emergency notification is laced with judgment. And yet, on Monday, they will post a cute stock photo of a light-skinned Black girl next to an Asian guy and caption it, 'We fight for inclusivity,' while their entire board of directors and C-suite is White, straight, and male. You can't wonder why you can't retain any people of color if you don't invest in the middle management that keeps them there! Do they even think about how this impacts their employees? Do they not realize some of their 'I&D talent' grew up in the communities they do pro bono work for? That community work serves their employees' friends, family, and support system! Are they so blind they can't see how systematic racism ripples through society, or do they care so little they are just keeping up appearances? I don't know which is worse!

"Oh, and don't get me started on how they only hire people of color for the Chief Inclusion Officer—you're telling me you need a C-suite individual who isn't your Human Resources Director who will help you actively recruit and retain people of color but not change anything about the company culture? Okay, great—please, write another book about how it only works when marginalized communities work for it. I just—"

The strung along sentences paused when Michael saw Leilani staring at him. Thinking.

"Hey, I'm sorry. I didn't mean to upset you. I know you're going through a lot and… it doesn't matter. How are you feeling?"

Michael had clearly been reading through another "how to help your partner deal with their abortion" article. He always used that tone when he was trying to figure out how to be gentle without coddling, careful while genuine, engaging in a real conversation while offering a safe space for her to not have to share anything at all.

"How I feel about…?"

Michael made sure to not get any closer, afraid she would become defensive if he pushed her too far.

"About George Floyd, the protests, and…" he prompted.

"And the abortion?" She knew he'd wanted to talk about it for a while now. Though she admired his dedication to care for her so deeply despite potentially disagreeing with her decision, she knew he wanted to know if she was going to be okay. Because he couldn't handle seeing her so broken. Sad. Uncomfortable. Disconnected.

"In some ways, the abortion was the least of my problems. I know it was the right thing for me to do but now I have to deal with the other consequences. I have a medical bill I need to figure out how to pay for and get used to my body now it has gone through—" she paused, searching for the right word, "changes. I need to own it. But it's not going to happen today or tomorrow."

She looked at the pictures she had hanging around: images of beautiful ebony children with pearly white smiles, clustered around her father who in turn looked tired but satisfied with life. Photos of Aisha's children surround the group pictures between the sisters with their father.

"And then, there are moments when I think about how much death surrounds us. The death of this virus. The death at the hands of cops. The death at the hands of doctors who ignore our symptoms. The death of the decision of who can get a hospital bed. There's so much death. So many Black bodies. They say the virus kills men more often than women, and it takes the life of diabetics, of those who are prone to heart disease and other genetic factors. Michael, that's me. Being Black makes you vulnerable to this disease. We have those predispositions because of the racism engrained in every institution. It goes as deep as a misdiagnosis, to the lack of access to medical facilities, to affordability of treatment, to prevention plans. BLM is fighting for equal access. But this death count is taking a toll on me. I can't..." Leilani didn't think she could continue. She wasn't okay. But how... what words could she use to explain it? What was she going through?

Leilani tossed the last part of her pizza and started to clean up the area around her. Michael started to collect the trash, but he kept eyeing Leilani, waiting for her to continue. Leilani placed her hands on either edge of the sink. She felt Michael's stare and shook her head before she spoke again.

"The firm wants me to represent the five Black people in this hundred-person firm. They didn't ask me. They didn't offer it to me; it was just assumed I would take it. Because why wouldn't I want to spend most of my afternoons explaining to my coworkers not to kill people like me? How what they say dramatically impacts how I'm able to manage today? And I don't want to talk about what is going on! Because I can't begin to process it. I can figure why they picked me. I'm the darkest one in the room. So I'm the obvious answer, right? But they'd say it's because I'm more of a 'seasoned' professional and know how to speak to a broader audience. In other words, I can dial down my 'Blackness,' and they want to show clients they care about Black people through me."

She could hear her downstairs neighbor hit her floor again and she ignored it, finally feeling some semblance of anger. "You know what's ridiculous? They can't bother to just hire more people of color. They need more people! It's not like they are making up roles. They have available spots—people are actually unemployed. Or point to the five 'new hires' who were interns who accepted the role a year ago. Sorry, no, that's not *actively recruiting*. Instead of telling me in every call they are angry for me and here for me, they should be working with HBCUs. I don't care you're angry! Just fix it! Fix everything! Fix the syst—"

When they heard more banging from the floor, Michael yelled down, "Will you just let her fucking talk!" At that, the banging stopped, and Michael continued to keep that same distance but looked at her intently, showing he was listening.

Leilani couldn't help but smile at him. She opened her arms to encourage an embrace.

As they held each other, she whispered into his shoulder. "I am done trying to pretend there's a system to work with. I'm tired."

***

Leilani grabbed her phone and set it beside her laptop. She sat back on her bed and rested her lower back on the multitude of decorative pillows, attempting to find a comfortable position. While she waited for her laptop to load the video chat application, Leilani continued to readjust her position before throwing them all on the ground. She hunched over her laptop and entered her credentials before a gentle chime indicated her video was live.

"Hey!" Leilani greeted a black screen; it looked like Brittany's camera was still off and her audio was on mute.

"Brittany, can you hear me?" Leilani adjusted her laptop again.

"Can you hear me now?" Brittany's crackled voice sounded through the application, sans video.

"Yes, I can. Can you hear me?" Leilani raised her voice, though it was shortly accompanied with two bangs from the floor. Leilani rolled her eyes, and out of the screen of the video feed she flipped off her floor.

"Are you okay? Oh, cute top by the way!" Brittany's voice came through a little clearer, though it still sounded like she was in a tunnel. Leilani looked down, having forgotten she was wearing a satin pink spaghetti strap blouse with matching short-shorts.

"Aw, thank you! There was a Victoria's Secret sale. Yeah, all good. Neighbor is just annoying me again."

"Estephania" appeared as a new box on the screen, and Nia's bright smile trailed not long after.

"Hey! Sorry I'm late. I've missed you guys!" Nia's face appeared, her onyx twists and sepia skin glistening on camera.

"Nia, did you get your hair done? It looks so good! You're glowing!" Leilani loved the gold detailing of the bands circling Nia's face. She couldn't help but wish to go into a hair salon and have her scalp massaged—even if the hairstyle didn't change.

Nia laughed and posed for them both. "I did! My mami did them for me. She's been practicing on my sister's hair and has gotten pretty good. Quarantine has made everybody a hairdresser."

"You look so cute Nia. And the red lips are really working for you!" Brittany's voice crackled again.

"Thanks! If you two keep hyping me up, I'm going have a bigger forehead than I already do. Where's Kat, by the way? She better not ditch us." Nia glanced at her phone and threw it upward. She rolled her eyes before sighing. "It's as if she heard me—Kat can't make it *again*. What's up with her? Is she dating someone new?" Nia leaned back against her headrest.

Leilani began to scroll through Kat's social media feeds as Brittany came up with her own theories. Leilani noted Kat seemed oddly absent from social media.

"Maybe she's not okay. The past two weeks have been really rough, to say the least. Maybe the stress caught up to her?" Leilani bit at the skin along her nails. Kat posted every day regardless if she left the house—there had to be a reason why she hadn't posted since Juneteenth.

"Well, she could have said something." Brittany's voice crackled through.

Nia shrugged. "I'd hope so. We've been friends for so long. It's a slap in the face to think she wouldn't trust us with something."

Leilani used her nails to continue to pick at the skin around her thumb. "It's not always about trust. She might need time to figure it out."

Nia rolled her head side to side and rotated her shoulders back. "Maybe. Ugh, my back is killing me from using my pillows as a desk."

Brittany's profile highlighted her name. "Tell me about it. My feet are killing me too. I swear my Health app freaked out when it saw how much I walked. Like damn, I know I only walk to the kitchen and back, but really? You *had* to call me out?"

Nia calmed her laughter and shook her head. "You're ridiculous. How was the protest in Chicago? I saw your story and it looked like there was a huge turnout."

Brittany's profile lit up again. "It was so good. We had some really great speakers talk and it was nice to feel people around me, especially people who were down for the cause. The music, the dancing, and the chanting was so fulfilling to my soul. But of course, everyone at work asked me if I was okay. Like... what? No, I'm not okay. That march made me feel a lot better, but until Black people stop getting shot and stop getting incarcerated, I'm not okay. I swear, those company emails about 'checking in on your local Black coworkers' are going to make me scream."

Leilani shook her head. It seemed no one knew what good manners looked like anymore. "Yeah, I've been selected to be the representative for these workshops with our clients at the firm and I don't get it. I feel like they are pouring all of these 'speaking engagements' because of the protests, but I don't know if they care about my career path or how I feel about it. I just keep getting nominated to do it when there's, like, five other Black women in an office of over a hundred people. It's been so frustrating, and I've had to basically say I have a health reason which is why I'm not well enough to do it—"

"Well, damn. I know we're hurting, but we need those opportunities." Nia held herself in a hug and continued. "Hopefully, you'll take them, Lani, and speak up for Black women wanting to pursue a career in law. I know you're hesitating about your next step professionally, but you're a great person. And the whole point is they are listening now, and we need to take those moments to speak our voice."

Right. Because of the lack of opportunities given to Black women, if she didn't take them, it meant one less for someone else.

"She's right. I know we're angry and want to say 'fuck you,' but we need to take every chance we get to change things. I know there are other Black women, but you said they were all new hires. Right, Leilani? Maybe that's why they are focusing on you. They want you to mentor them, and even though we want to shut everything down, we can't do it without helping others up." Brittany sighed. "It just sucks we need to do that. This is why I had to risk my asthmatic ass getting COVID. If this virus doesn't kill me, the world's bullshit will."

Leilani nodded and grabbed her water to take a sip. No wonder Kat wasn't joining anymore. Kat was always around for a good time, but Nia and Brittany... they were hardheaded. They want to boil the ocean. But Leilani wasn't sure she had the energy to make it through the day, much less take down the entire system. Leilani made her sips long, giving her a chance to look at her reflection in the glass. She moved her face away from the glass, letting the last bit of water sit at the bottom of her mouth, but continued to look down the glass and her reflection, unsettled by the gnawing feeling in her stomach.

Yet another feeling that would eat her up at night without words to describe it.

"She's probably thinking about Michael again."

Brittany's voice jolted Leilani into focus. "I'm sorry, what?"

Nia laughed and shook her head. "My god, that boy has you caught up. What did he text you? Any weekend plans? I mean, who has a concept of time anymore, but I'm guessing he's taking you out for your birthday. No?"

Right. She had forgotten about her birthday in the middle of all of the protests, father's anticipatory heart attack, and…

"Um, yeah. We are renting out a place in Tahoe. Actually, a friend is lending us his cabin since you can't get an Airbnb in some parts. But we'll mostly stay inside. I'm prediabetic, and Michael has asthma, so I don't want to push our exposure." Leilani was pretty excited she was getting some relief from being inside her house all the time. The thought brought a smile to her face.

"Aw, that's so cute. Well yeah, keep yourselves safe first. And make sure to bring love gloves too. You don't want to accidentally leave with a different kind of birthday present too," Nia teased. Brittany chortled while Nia knocked on wood on Leilani's behalf.

"My god, Nia!" Brittany's laughter was still going strong after a minute.

"I'm just saying." Nia shrugged and started to go on a rant that, once again, her boyfriend didn't understand the concept of thoughtful gift-giving.

As Brittany and Leilani pretended to listen attentively to Nia, Leilani looked down at her glass of water that was still half full and half empty.

***

"Even if I had the scrawniest butt you ever saw?" Leilani asked, her eyes wide.

Michael sighed and turned slowly. He pulled her into a deep kiss, dipping her as he did so.

"Hun, even if your ass concaved and people asked us if you lost it in a shark attack, I would love you and proudly scream, 'My girlfriend's ass does shit you guys would only dream of.'"

At that, Leilani had to kiss him and loop her hands around his neck.

"Aww, you're such a good liar. I've trained you well."

"Do all women love coming up with the weirdest scenarios to test their man's devotion?"

"Nope." She walked around him to steal a slice of pepperoni pizza off his plate. "It's a tool used to see how well you can lie to us when you cheat. You're passing with flying colors, by the way."

"You monster!" He faked a gasp. "At least take a proper bite of the pizza if you're taking a 'peperone.'"

"How many times do I have to tell you it's *pepperoni*, not peperone?"

"Give me a break, will you? I didn't get reclassified as a fluent English speaker until eighth grade."

"Again, I question the quality of Chicago's education system."

"Really, Leilani? You grew up in Houston."

"First of all, it's Katy, Texas. But you're wrong. I used my dad's boss's address and attended the better school ten miles away."

"Check your privilege, Leilani—not all of us had parents with bosses who advocated for their employees' kids." He laughed and made his way back on the couch.

"I have to say, I appreciate Josue. He could be hard on my dad, but he understood the struggle. You know, his family came from Mexico and started one of the largest property management places in the county. He made sure my sisters and I had a chance to go to college like his girls and helped Candice, Makellah, Zoë, and me transfer to their district in middle school."

"That's really nice of him. He's the guy who helped your dad with the citizenship application. Right?"

"Yeah. He sponsored him even though he knew he could take a financial loss if my dad switched employers shortly after getting the visa. But he knew my dad was a devoted worker, and he was right. Twenty-one years later and he's still going strong."

"No wonder your dad wasn't trying to rest for long after the heart attack a few months ago." He was still replying in between mouthfuls of food.

"Yeah, my dad can't sit still. In some ways, I think he's looking to compensate Josue for helping him out."

"It's hard not to. I know my parents would be the same way if their bosses sponsored them." He frowned. "But the factory makes a lot of money using undocumented labor, and there's no incentive to help them out. Especially now. Despite all the risks they take on by just going to work. I'm glad they have jobs, but still..."

At that, Michael paused. He stopped eating and left the plate on his lap.

Leilani opened her mouth to comfort him, but Michael continued.

"You know, they always say once you reach the American Dream, you rise above poverty and all of its problems. It's a promise—if you make it and pull yourself up from the boot-straps, you will make a life for yourself. Not a rich one, but one that guarantees safety for your family. Food on the table. Education to pursue a degree. But no one tells you you're only going up one rung of the ladder—one rung of hundreds. And no one tells you it's even easier to go back down. But it's a contract: no one reads the fine print."

"But you're helping them now. You help them financially—you give them reassurance the sacrifices they made were worth it. For you and Joanna."

"But I just graduated from undergrad last year—I don't have my shit together at all. I've just started to build my savings and pay into my 401K. I had to copy my 'new joiner' teammate's retirement allocation because I added 2 percent to each item." He shook his head. "Fuck, I don't even remember what the hell I did in high school—it's all a blur. People think I just want to share my 'journey' to college, but really, I don't remember. I mostly blocked it out. I just remember being tired all of the time. My semester abroad at Morocco was the first time I really felt hope for my future, I could actually do this. It was the first time I looked up. But it makes the fall that much harder."

She inched closer to him but gave him space to speak. She didn't want her touch to make him assume she wanted him to calm down. Rage, in all forms, demands to be acknowledged.

Still, he needed to know he wasn't alone.

"You're still figuring things out, but you *are* helping. You're helping them now you are self-sufficient. And Joanna will graduate soon and help you care for them."

"But she has a shit load of loans she's going to carry from undergrad and graduate school. I'm the one with the lucrative job; I'm the one who needs to make sure our parents can retire. I can't even put them on my medical plan because it only works from parents to children and not the other way around…" He clenched his hands into fists. "And I hate my job most days, but I know I can't leave—and what if something happens before Joanna graduates? I'd need to fly back and take care of my sister, aunt, and cousin, on top of dealing with the house. My dad had someone cosign the home loan, and I'd need to transfer the debt onto me and keep paying the cosigner for helping us out. Then there's my parents. I would need to send money to Lebanon so they aren't struggling alone. It's not like I can fly there often with clothes and things they need. Especially in a pandemic."

"You could help your aunt by letting them live there—"

"But I would have to deal with all the taxes that come with it. I wouldn't be able to afford the mortgage and would be under crushing student loans and mortgage payments. I would need to be there and help her out. My aunt raised us while my parents worked; I can't leave her alone. It's my turn." He paused again and stared at the pillow behind her. "I would have to leave California, my job… and you."

Leilani tried to ignore the idea of Michael leaving her— she needed to help him out of this spiral.

"What makes you think they wouldn't let you transfer to another city?"

"The company isn't large but you have to network with the teams to get a transfer. I know people in San Francisco, but I hardly know anyone from the Chicago office."

"Michael, they can make exceptions—talk to HR or an employee resource group. Even your boss, someone will work with you. You're one of the top consultants on your team. They will understand the need for a transfer."

He laughed, humorlessly. "We're talking about the same boss, right? The one who uses the R-word? He isn't exactly the most understanding. All the conversations about immigration are done through the Latinx and Black employee groups—I'm neither."

"There has to be *someone*. Honestly, just saying you have a family emergency that requires a relocation should be enough. I can talk to my team; they need pro bono work, and they would help you and your family. And the house might be something that can be managed if your aunt is able to work. Your cousin is in eighth grade, right? He might not need as much caretaking as you're expecting. If you consider your savings and the adjustment in salary the company would give you, you'd actually be able to cover a mortgage once you refinance it. And when Joanna starts working, she can help send a few dollars to your parents. Plus, they could find new jobs and live with your grandmother. Michael, you're not alone."

She could feel him release the tension in his shoulders as soon as she placed her arm around him. His chest trembled twice as it lowered before rising again. She tucked his head into her shoulder.

They stayed quiet for a moment before he finally voiced it. "What about us?"

She breathed him in. She could feel her heartbeat in her hands. "We... would figure it out. Who knows? Maybe I drove you away with one of my stupid questions before you had to deal with this, or..."

He smiled into her shoulder. "Are you saying you'd move to Chicago? A city you said 'God designed to make people not live there.' You must really love me."

"I didn't say that, but someone thinks highly of themself. I could visit you somewhere in between and have virtual date nights. We did it for over two months. I think we'll manage. First thing is first: nothing is happening right now, and we don't need to worry about it. Same with your family—we have a plan, but we don't need to live in a hypothetical. Let's handle one crisis at a time."

He held her closer.

She couldn't tell him she feared the same thing. She didn't dare say it out loud. Their world was fragile and growing even more so by the moment.

"Together?"

"Always."

"Even, say, a 'meet the family video chat?'"

She tried to steady her heart. She knew. Damn, she knew.

"When are they asking us to meet?"

"Soon."

Which, of course, meant in the next few weeks.

That would mean she would need to introduce her family to him soon after that. Somehow, Leilani didn't think it could be more poorly timed to see all of her life collide in the middle of a pandemic.

What could go right?

***

Dear Michael,

I must love you if I'm doing this. Meeting your parents scares the living hell out of me. It's too hard to explain, and I'm more afraid to write it down, but I will tell you this: being accepted by them will mean everything to me...

BELEN, LOS ANGELES— JULY 2020

"It's incredible to see the energy of all of these young people take action. It's really getting through people's heads it's crucial to determine the election outcome. Not just the presidency, but the ballots, the senators, the congressmen. Everything!"

Belen had been going off for the last thirty minutes about the virtual conference she organized and seeing the positive outcome. She wasn't given much time to take the original planning and transform the virtual event into a three-day affair with special guests. She loved engaging with rising college freshman, but she was more excited about young professionals sharing their stories as they've embarked their own way of advocacy at companies and in government.

Axel wasn't interested, but he didn't bother to interrupt since he was trying to avoid doing his homework anyway. Listening to Belen rattle off was at least more entertaining than literature assignments.

"And so many of them are going to protests and were speaking about the experience. I wish I could join them."

Axel twirled his pencil with his right hand and tried to do the same thing on his left.

Belen glanced at him. "I can't get you and Mom sick. Anyway, it's downtown, and I don't really want to take public transportation to get there."

"Then use Mom's car. She's using the USPS truck anyway. She doesn't use her own car to get to work." Axel dropped the pencil, which flew across the room. As he walked over to pick it up, he remembered. "Oh, that's right—you can't drive. Aren't you a little too old to not know how to drive?"

He missed Belen's reaction. "Excuse you. I've never had the need to learn how to drive. Mom always said she didn't really think I needed to learn." Still ruffled by the snide comment, Belen scoffed. "Anyway, I'm better off not wrecking the car."

Axel turned around and scrunched his face. "What are you referring to? Mom taught me how to drive."

Belen shook off the comment. "It's not essential—"

"How do you even get to school? On the bus, or do you just hitch a ride with friends? And—"

At the rustle of keys, Axel's interrogation ended.

"Hola, Mami. How was work? Here are your sandals." Belen grabbed her mother's tote bag and began unpacking the remnants of her mother's lunch.

"Ugh, same as always: long." Her mother never really wanted to talk about her job, and Belen wondered if it was because of the working conditions or if her mother was too scared to complain and have a karmic energy take the small amount of stability they had.

"How was yours?"

"Oh, Mami. I spoke to Socorro, and she's an incredible student."

"Now you've set her off." Axel groaned and finished setting his mother's plate before going to the bathroom to play games on his phone.

Belen had been ranting about the DACA student whose desire for an education "was unlike any of her other students." Her mother always sympathized with the undocumented community and admired Socorro's dedication to persevere despite her family's circumstances. Belen connected to Socorro every week, sometimes more—definitely beyond what was required. Even as Belen's schedule became increasingly tight with the organization and dedication to her internship, she made time to discuss Socorro's dreams.

"Mira esa niña.[18] I've always said it. Those who have papers don't have a right to be homeless. They know English—well. They are able to work, have benefits, access to healthcare. And for what? To waste their days getting drunk behind the motels near the high school. I've seen them when I would drop you off, Belen. It was so disappointing. I've always told the parents who ask me about you. Those who want to go to college, go."

Though she had heard this rant many times over, Belen couldn't help but be frustrated by it. It wasn't quite that simple.

"Mami, look. I'm not the rule for college admissions—I'm the exception. That's why it's called the American Dream: I've worked hard, and I know kids who were much smarter than me. But it's the circumstances that caused them to not attend college or drop out. It's their situation. I know my mentees

---

18   Translation: Look at that girl.

want to go to college so badly, but they're lost. Some don't realize they don't even meet the college requirements. Or their high schools only focus on increasing their graduation rate—not their career options post K-12."

Her mother contemplated it for a moment and shrugged. "I don't know. I immigrated here and served this nation to make sure my kids had a brighter future. I see how people are able to improve themselves here." Leslie took a breath. "Despite everything that's wrong in the world."

"The American Dream is a myth. It's like Mulan: we're raised on this legend if you work hard enough, you can overcome anything. But many of us don't—and it's not from the lack of trying. Remember how hard it was for me to get my assignments printed, so we had mi tía[19] Nina send us her typewriter? Some kids don't have that. They don't have access to a computer right now. We're lucky Axel even has a computer distributed by the school."

"Speaking of, where is Axel? Axel!"

Leslie and Belen heard the toilet flush and the faucet turn on before Axel emerged into the room.

"Did you finish your homework?"

"No. You two were talking too loud for me to focus. I was on my phone." He started to slump forward and walked to his chair.

Belen sighed. "Axel, finish your homework."

Leslie walked over to the bathroom to rinse up before dinner.

"Belen, I *can't*. I don't know how to do it."

Belen walked over and reviewed the assignment over his shoulder: an essay on Edgar Allan Poe's *Annabel Lee*. The

---

19 Translation: My aunt

prompt asked about the objective summary of the events in the text, identifying rhyme patterns and the effects of repetition, and how the tone explained the true meaning of the poem. Axel had filled out the first two questions, but the latter were left blank.

Suddenly the document hit a network error—likely due to the fact the Xbox was online at the same time. While their mother ate, Belen and Axel worked to troubleshoot their Wi-Fi connection and finally work on the questions. Though Belen tried to get Axel to understand the use of rhymes and repetition, Axel grew more and more frustrated and moved his hands back and forth.

Finally, Belen's mother chirped in. "Axel, can't you ask the teacher? Or a classmate?"

Their mother's comment triggered an unexpected reaction. "No one likes me! They work on everything together and never include me." Axel began to bite the sides of his nails and grow more quiet. Their family knew the bullying was never easy on Axel, but he seemed to brush it off easily. Officially having virtual summer school classes with new classmates in high school while still being rejected must have made Axel acutely aware he was different. Her mother's face read the same determination: they would have to speak with the high school to set up an Individualized Educational Plan soon.

"Hey, Axel, I think it helps if we listen to this poem."

"I've already said it out loud and I don't get it, Belen." He chewed on the side of his thumb more aggressively.

"I actually meant to watch a movie."

Axel stopped picking at the dead skin but didn't look at her. "Really?"

"There's a movie I think might help you understand it. Have you seen *Holes*?"

***

If there was one thing about Belen, it was she always had a plan of attack. You can blame it on her mother's military discipline ("You'll take the bathroom, Axel will take care of the living room, and I will take charge of the kitchen. We will regroup when it's done—questions?") or her insistent need to be the best at everything she did. In either case, she tackled everything with a well thought out methodology, supported by at least three different sources and responses to any counter arguments at the flip of a hand. Thus began phase one: breakfast.

Axel was still cranky about being woken up, but the promise of a plateful of bacon kept him in good enough spirits until the promise was delivered on. In between a pour of pancake batter, Belen made her mother a strong cup of coffee, left it in her mother's room, and kissed her temple as Axel finished up the last few pieces of breakfast.

Her mother emerged a few moments later with a damp face and coffee in hand. She didn't question the hustle and bustle of the morning and enjoyed her breakfast on one of the few days off she had. Once Belen was satisfied with stuffing her brother and mother with food, she had Axel wash the dishes while she proceeded with phase two: deep cleaning.

Despite her mother's protests of having Belen and Axel swarm around her cleaning the entire house, ("*Ya deja eso allí. Me están desesperando en mi día de descanso.*"[20]) Belen continued to scrub the stove top and replaced the gas stove covers with a new sheet of aluminum foil ("*deja que te*

___
20   Translation: Leave it be. You're making me anxious on my day off [due to their hustle and bustle].

ayudemos.[21] You don't get days off, and we don't want you on your feet.") Instead, she sent her mom off to the living room to rest and catch up her telenovelas. By 10:30 a.m., the heat started to warm the living room and soft snores echoed through the space. Axel and Belen wrapped up their chores quietly but kept the television on.

Though Axel wanted to watch Minecraft videos for the rest of the day, Belen promised to watch a movie of his choice if he went along with her Fourth of July plans. Unenthused, he followed her to the backyard and into phase three: gardening. She hoped she could get Axel into a new hobby that motivated him to get some sunlight. Especially now her mom had less time at home, she had high hopes the garden would manifest into something Axel could invest time to other than movies or YouTube.

They both stopped in front of their mission and assessed their plan of attack. Her mother had placed new plants in clean Kirkland detergent buckets and would eventually transfer them into the garden. Leslie would say plants, like humans, needed time to acclimate and would wait a few days to make the transition. Belen decided they would leave her mother's buckets of plants untouched for now. There was limited space between the chili peppers, aloe vera, lemongrass, rosemary, basil, and wide-leaf oregano plants growing, presumably for the new additions. Without disrupting the roots, Belen worked the land to show a divide between Axel's side and her side of the garden. However, there was a gap between the plants and the concrete wall, with a small wooden fence keeping the herbs and peppers away from the soil near the wall. She decided to have Axel start clearing

---

21 Translation: Let us help you

out the weeds, and she started on working in the extra soil she ordered on Amazon. Though she felt bad for contributing toward overwhelming the delivery service people, she knew her mom would be more upset about her fetching soil in stores to do one of her "new age parenting" experiments.

Belen watched as Axel cleared out a few weeds near the wall, stepping close to the fenced portion.

"Be careful with the aloe plants. Mom will be upset if you hurt her babies."

"They're not babies. And I know. I accidentally threw out some dirty water near the garden and she yelled at me."

"Mom is very particular."

Belen left it at that and continued to work on adding the new soil with the existing humus. The quiet labor with the heat warming their backs would usually feel unbearable, but the cool breeze made it tolerable. Light music from their neighbor's stereo added to the tranquility of the day. Once they were ready, she let Axel plant each of the sunflower seeds as she followed behind him, watering can in tow.

Axel moved to mist the remaining plants with the hose, his face contorted.

"What's wrong?" Belen started to clean up the workspace, glancing back at him.

"Do you think they'll grow? Don't they need to be planted in the spring?"

True. She probably should have looked into that. But with everything going on, she had figured with the Valley's mild temperature, it wouldn't matter.

"They should be able to grow in the summer. Why wouldn't they?"

"Sunflowers require a delicate balance of sunlight, soil, and watering. They also need to be big enough to survive the winter." Axel's matter-of-fact tone always irked her. She knew he didn't mean to sound condescending, but it was hard to keep her temper in check.

"I think it's fine. It's not rocket science."

"You're right. It's called botany."

Their small squabble attracted the attention of the neighbor. The mirth in her voice was evident as she interrupted the tiff. "He is right. Ideally, you should plant sunflower seeds in late April."

Belen ignored Axel's pointed look, and she instead focused on the wall and little hair bun that poked above it.

"However, it's Southern California, and the lack of seasons shouldn't hinder the growth of your plants too much. Though I would recommend you water them in the early morning or late evening so the water doesn't evaporate."

Axel turned off the water. "Thank you, ma'am. I told you, Belen. Should we stop then?"

After some scuffle, an elderly Asian woman's head popped over the fence. "You're welcome. And no, if the plants haven't been watered today, it would serve you well to do it now. And please don't call me ma'am. I'm Sherry."

"Oh, like the fruit."

"More like the alcohol. My parents were alcoholics and fond of the Spanish."

"Spanish spirits?"

"That too."

Belen couldn't help but chuckle despite Axel's evident confusion. Ms. Sherry had an eccentricity that reminded her of her mom's energy. Belen sat back on one of the lawn chairs and watched as Axel learned about planting and somehow transition into face reading. Ms. Sherry continued to view

Axel from a distance, asking him to slightly turn his face to get a better reading.

"Hm. You have a good set of eyes."

Axel nodded. "My optometrist thinks so too."

Ms. Sherry laughed and shook her head. "I mean the eyelids are broad and full. You have large pupils and clear whites. It means you have a spirit and energy. Good round and plump chin. It symbolizes wealth."

Axel smiled. Ms. Sherry's smile tugged down from one corner.

"Your eyebrows are dark, thick and smooth. But it looks like you have a deep scar cutting through one of them."

Belen chimed in. "I think he hurt himself as a toddler. He was always so hyperactive."

Ms. Sherry nodded. "I see."

Axel ignored the lack of explanation about his eyebrows. "So is this similar to what Walter Mercado did? He's the guy who would talk about the horoscopes on the morning news."

"I suppose so. Faces tell us so much about another person, even before they speak. I suppose people who see their birthdays could say the same about them." Ms. Sherry continued to explain the origins of face reading while Belen kept watch from her seat.

Belen couldn't help but witness the interaction: Axel animatedly talking about yet another Netflix documentary he had watched where conspiracy theorists believed health organizations purposely kept people sick, and Ms. Sherry nodding and asking questions from time to time. Even after Axel rudely refuted back on some of Ms. Sherry's points, the elderly lady looked unbothered and kept him engaged. Belen had to appreciate her—most teachers wrote him off for being insensitive, which caused Axel to feel lonelier. Still, the heat was increasing, and she felt bad for keeping the old woman under the scorching California sun.

Feeling her throat tickle from the lack of saliva, Belen got up and approached Axel. "It's getting really hot outside, and we don't want to give you a heatstroke, Ms. Sherry."

"Oh, don't worry. It's worth it if I get to talk to someone. My kids check in on me twice a week, but living alone makes me batty. But since we're gardening buddies, here."

Ms. Sherry momentarily disappeared and reappeared with a small basket full of cherries. Axel ran toward the basket that swung over the fence.

Remembering his manners, Axel smiled at his neighbor. "Thank you. We'll share whatever we manage to keep alive."

"Thanks for the vote of confidence, Axel."

"I have no confidence this will grow if I keep following your directions, Belen."

Annoyed, Belen thanked Ms. Sherry and promised to disinfect and return the basket with chili peppers.

Somewhat exhausted, Axel looked ready to nap. Belen forced him into phase four: hot dogs.

"I thought you liked hot dogs?"

"I'm tired, Belen. You've had me working all day on a holiday, that's also a Saturday. It's my only break during summer school! What kind of teenager doesn't let kids sleep in on their day off?"

"Get used to it, kiddo. However, I do owe you a movie of your choice. But only the ones on Disney-Plus."

"I thought it was my choice?"

"Yeah, you get to choose from a selection of movies. I don't want to see you repeat anymore inappropriate movie quotes though."

"You're saying this because I quoted *Stepbrothers* once—"

"Three times. And yeah, that's exactly why I'm doing it." She wrapped the sausages with bacon, letting it heat up on the pan. Axel set the table and peeked into the refrigerator from time to time. Her mother had outdone herself with the Mosaic Milk Gelatin, lining the circumference with strawberries. She was still on the phone with her sisters in Miami but moved into the bedroom once Axel turned on the TV. Usually, he would have streamed a movie, but today he left on the local news, knowing their mom's favorite competition show would be on soon.

However, a special broadcast populated. Claims Vanessa Guillen was sexually harassed before her disappearance yield "no credible reports." Two months later her body had been identified. Two months and several deaths of women of color, and still this is all they were able to do: conclude her death. The more she let her thoughts consume her, the more she kept flipping the sausages with aggression. She didn't see Axel stare at her or her mom come out of the bedroom. They kept repeating the tearful family speech Vanessa's family delivered.

"Oye, ten cuidado.[22] No one goes, 'Oh Ms. Leslie, here is free sartenes!'[23] You are beating the damn frying pan the way I'm going to grab you if you don't calm down."

Belen didn't register her mother's complaint.

"They don't care, Mom! They are just passively repeating information to us."

"What are you talking about?"

"They identified her body. It's hers. But they are dismissing her family's claims about Vanessa being sexually assaulted!"

---

22   Translation: Hey, be careful.
23   Translation: Frying pan

"And that's why you batter my cooking utensils? I'm not shitting rolls of bills when I go to the toilet. I work long hours at a shitty job with USPS. Especially during the holidays when companies give holiday specials. They have me working double shifts as it is."

"Okay. I'm sorry. But can you believe this? How the government recruits from our middle schools, promises a better life, and does nothing to care for the soldiers when they report abuse? How? How could this even happen?"

Her mother turned her back on her and helped Axel finish setting the table. Belen continued:

"And it's not the first time they've failed us. At every damn level, they fail us! If we go to the hospital because I need birth control for my dysmenorrhea, my nurse tells me to close my legs. If I try to get an education, I'm accused of taking other student's money because apparently their school tuition feeds into my scholarship fund. If I choose to serve this country, I am murdered for refusing to let the White man abuse me. Even as an EMT, I get shot in my sleep! Why should I even fucking bother?"

Her mother slammed her glass down, causing Axel and Belen to shake.

"¿Y que quieres que haga?[24] I know you're angry, but I've always taught you to rise above it. You can't complain to the whole world and expect them to change. You still have more than others do. Are you going to stop eating because someone criticizes you on how you eat?" she yelled.

"Mom, you're not understanding. It does impact us. Speaking against racism isn't complaining; it's necessary for

---

24 Translation: And what do you want me to do?

systematic change. It's our right to fight for equal treatment! Those protests demonstrate we matter."

"Those protestors don't care about us! You said it. They are not about us. Black people riot and release anger and don't do shit."

"Mom, we are Black people! Brown people matter. Asian people matter. Latinx matters. Everyone matters! But objectively, it's worse for Black people."

"Then tell me where they were when Latinos were fighting for undocumented people? A ver, dime.[25] We show up for everyone. And no one is there. You said it yourself. No one is here to help us. But sitting on our asses like they are doesn't put food on the table, doesn't keep you guys fed, doesn't pay the mortgage. I'll support it when I see Blacks walk alongside us."

"They did! We did! I know you have this whole 'mejorar la raza'[26] mentality, but you need to acknowledge we are Afro-Latinos, Mami. Tío Junior[27] is your second cousin and part of the Garifuna tribe, yet he calls you Black!"

"Being Mulatto in Honduras and being Black here is different. They don't accept us here. They call us allies—or have you ever heard them call you Black?"

Belen kept quiet and lowered the heat of the frying pan. She looked at her beige arms. Though it looked ashy from forgetting to put on moisturizer, the golden undertones of her skin reminded her of the countless times her classmates asked her where she summered.

---

25 Translation: Now, tell me
26 Translation: "Improve the race"; phrase implies that the *Blanqueamiento* (whitening) practice moves person(s) toward a supposed "ideal whiteness" for social, political, and/or economic benefits
27 Translation: Uncle

Leslie took a breath.

"I'm not being racist. I'm following the cues of this country. Let me see them do something about Latinos in this country and stop the death, the children in cages, the separation of families." Her mother started to leave the room, but she instead she stopped and turned to Belen one more time. "Black people may be treated less than others, but at least no one questions their status. But being an 'other' isn't going to stop me, make me cry, or hold me back. That's not why I came here. It's not why your father's parents brought him here from Guatemala. This is not how we raised you." And with that, she finally left the room.

Belen wiped a stray tear away and slowly looked around her. Half completed buns and sausages were scattered across the small counter space. From the other end of the connected dining room, Axel had gotten halfway done with his bowl of cereal, his headphones securely locking him away from her fight. She finished preparing the dinner and knocked on her mother's door.

Leslie smiled and chided Belen. "Ay niña, I told you I could have ordered."

Even so, Belen's mother served herself three of the street style hot dogs and waited for Belen to sit down before praying. After they gave grace, Leslie took generous mouthfuls of food before giving small talk to Belen.

"And how's Maggie? Is she still with that boyfriend of hers? Charlie?"

Belen fiddled with the same initial bite as she watched her mother start on the second hot dog.

"She's good. Charlie is okay, but he misses her. I half expect him to fly out of Texas to see her, but who knows."

In the middle of a bite, Leslie covered her mouth but continued talking. "They didn't stay in their apartment?"

"Technically their apartment was through residential living, so they had to give it up when the university sent everyone home. So Maggie stayed at her parents' house in San Diego, but Charlie had to go back to Texas."

"Hm. And they don't plan to see each other?"

Belen took her third bite, too exhausted to take another, and shrugged. "Who knows. They haven't given us reopening plans. The school would be pretty stupid to reopen though."

Leslie munched on her last bite of the meal and began to clean the crumbs around her plate.

"Well, I wish them the best. But I am glad you've always been goal oriented and focused on what matters most: studies and graduating. Do you know what pride I have in telling your abuelita[28] of everything you've accomplished?"

Leslie wiped her mouth and came around the dining table to hug Belen from behind.

"I am so proud of you and everything you fight for. I see such big things to come from you. But focus first on your studies. The world's problems will continue to be there once you graduate."

Belen held her mother's arms to her, tucking her face into them. Her mother tightened her hold and kissed the top of her head.

As they cleaned up, Leslie and Belen fell in an easy silence. Though Belen always appreciated her mother did work to make amends with her, she felt heavier from the conversation.

After getting ready for bed and tucking in Axel, Belen walked inside her mother's room and asked Leslie if she

---

28 Translation: grandma

could spend that night in her bed. As they gave each other a blessing and said goodnight, the household fell asleep to the sounds of fireworks and dogs barking. It wasn't until the witching hour it happened.

The scream.

Only a sudden shake warned Belen before the strangled scream erupted from her mother's mouth. Belen couldn't help responding to the scream with one of her own. Her mother had her eyes closed and was twitching, as if the tiger blanket was holding her down. Her pillow was soaked in either tears or sweat, maybe both. Despite Belen's instinct to shake her mother awake, she forced herself to gently lay her hand on her mother's arms.

"¡Ama, despiértate!"[29] Belen pleaded with her mother as she rubbed Leslie's arms. Slowly working her way onto Leslie's shoulders, the gentle massages slowly stirred her mother.

"¡Cipote, te estaba gritando hace tiempo![30] I couldn't move to pinch you. Por Dios, I couldn't fucking take it."

"What were you dreaming about? You scared the hell out of me!"

"¡Cállate, que el güiro esta durmiendo!"[31]

Her mother had turned around and flipped her pillow-case. Belen lowered her voice and repeated the question.

"It's a nightmare… and we have to wait until it's noon to talk about it." Leslie still hadn't turned to look at Belen, but she felt Belen nested against her back.

"Mami, you always say that and never tell me."

---

29 Translation: Ma, wake up!
30 Translation: [Honduran slang] Child, I've been screaming for a while!
31 Translation: [Honduran slang] Shut up, the kid is asleep!

"Exactly. Bad dreams will go away and never manifest."

She raised herself up on one elbow and sighed. "Ama,[32] if you want to sleep tonight, you need to tell me."

Her mother glanced over her shoulder. "Te sueno para que te bajes."[33]

Belen rolled her eyes.

"Look. I know you don't want to talk about it, but what if it happens again? How can I help you? It doesn't feel like this isn't the first time it happened." The lack of response prompted her to continue. "Was it because of Vanessa Guillen?"

"Good night."

Leslie's curt response made Belen recoil and flip around. A few moments later, her mother sighed.

"It happens more because of her. Vanessa. But I've always had these nightmares."

She shifted over and looked at her mother. The streetlights illuminated the small bedroom window, and the warm light only landed on her mother's shoulder, leaving the rest of her in shadow.

"Being foreign born and being in the military wasn't an easy combination. I was proud to fight for this country. Your abuelita came here on her own with my sisters and me, knowing my brothers wouldn't make it out of Honduras. I wanted to show I loved this country and earned my right to be here." The clock ticked by at least sixty seconds before she continued. "Your dad was very sweet, but I didn't feel the same way he did for me. And he respected that. But others weren't like him."

Belen held her mother's fist and stayed silent.

---

32 Translation: Ma
33 Translation: [false threat] I'll hit you so you change that attitude.

Despite the remnants of sleep lacing her voice, Leslie spoke clearly and quietly.

"I got cut pretty bad when they tried to hold me down, but I'm from Santa Barbara, and we learn not to fear machetes. Better to be dead than to have them hold what they tried to do over my head. I told your dad and he wanted to march in there and report every single one of those malditos.[34] But it would mean losing our military careers. So instead, we married. Even while pregnant, they didn't stop. I had to take a medical leave due to complications with my pregnancy—the stress was starting to hurt you. So I had to discharge under medical pretenses. Your dad always protected me despite... you know how I am. He was my best friend, my partner; we were one team. And I keep seeing him."

"The guy who tried to—"

"No, not him. Your father," she took a deep breath. "As a woman, you learn to cry silently and alone. But your father would never let me cry alone, and even now he joins me in my dreams. He tells me to keep living for you both, and I tell him he's an idiot. I'm a soldier—my body is to protect others. And he laughs. It haunts me. Because he's always bloodied, with bruises and gash wounds from the car crash. When he was taken away from us... he threw his arm over me to stop the air bag from hitting my belly mid-crash so one of us stayed alive to protect you and Axel. You were so young and probably don't remember the accident. But I lay at night, remembering how I held my belly while your dad's cold arm laid on me."

When her mother shakes, Belen moves to cuddle her.

"It's just a nightmare, Mami. You're here with me. With us."

---

34 Translation: cursed/damned ones

"Of course. I know it's a nightmare. It was too real. Too tragically beautiful. Too far away."

They continued in that embrace, saturating their pillows with fresh tears. And as Belen held her mother to her more fiercely, she sang the lullaby she grew up with:

"Duérmase mi niña, duérmase ya. Porque si no se duerme, se la comerán. Ah rurururaca, ah rurrú, duérmase ya."[35]

Belen couldn't recall dreaming that night, but she remembered feeling a strong embrace holding her mother and her together.

---

35 Translation: [Lullaby] Sleep my darling [girl], sleep now. If you don't sleep, you'll be eaten. Sleep now.

OLIVIA, SCOTTSDALE—
JULY 2020

Finding out an account is frozen is never fun. Especially during an economic depression.

But hearing it from her mother? Olivia could have screamed. Apparently, their uncle was really serious about this inheritance—Olivia's allocated inheritance, specifically—and froze her account. The only joy of hearing from her mother was knowing how the progress of her safety net was going.

However, it meant her mother would go into tangents where Olivia would be forced to follow along.

"I've never understood that. You know?"

Olivia blinked hard, trying to figure out what her mother was asking her. Week after week, they went through an endless cycle of gossip, understanding the internet, watching Olivia's weight gain and career failures, more gossip, the rare and an oddly endearing piece of advice, understanding how to use her phone, Olivia's lack of love life… So much for avoiding contact.

"Hello?"

"Yeah? Sorry, my connection was going out. What did you say?" Olivia rolled her eyes as she filed her nails. Her mother's voice made it hard to multi-task.

"Hm, it's the second time this week. It must be because of that god awful apartment you live in. Remind me again why you needed to move to Arizona? I told you, everyone forgot—"

"Mom! Please. I'm begging you to let it go." Olivia adjusted the volume of her AirPods, afraid even her mother's raspy voice could vibrate throughout the apartment.

"I'm just saying, Olivia. It's not that bad. No one is talking about it. Hell, the Walkers have bigger issues, like their lack of funding, broken credibility, and crippling debt. It's too bad. I really like Caroline."

Olivia winced. Even with everything that happened, her mother still found a way to hurt her; to demonstrate how Caroline was everything she wasn't. Every week, the comment dug in deeper, to the point where her mother's voice would chase Olivia in her dreams.

Olivia felt her eyes burn. "What were you asking me before? Before my shitty Scottsdale apartment facing the pools when we momentarily lost connection?"

"Right! How are people dating nowadays? Are people video calling?"

"I guess it depends on where you are. Starting tomorrow, I'm not supposed to leave the house anymore because they've paused the reopening, busting any plans to get out of this miserable heat. I can't even imagine how hot it'll get in July."

"Oh, they've stopped everything? Well, take advantage to tan your legs. They're starting to look pasty again."

"How are you even seeing them?" Olivia began to scroll through her IG followers and search for her mom until she heard her mother laugh.

"You think I would follow you? I saw it from Katrina's phone when she came to visit. Apparently, you've been gathering quite a crowd down there. I'm glad you found a spot to replot yourself in. Like a sunflower, just looking for the light in the situation."

Olivia felt herself swell knowing her mom saw the potential for her business. "Thanks, Mom. I really appreciate it. I think I could—"

"Oh wait, Olivia, I forgot to tell you the best part. Miranda, Katrina's boyfriend's baby sister, is so obsessed with you. She really started to freak out when Katrina told her I was your mom. You should video chat with her!"

"That's so sweet! Wait, when did this all happen?"

Olivia heard her mom moving and the clacking of her heels across the marbled floor.

"Oh, I think maybe this past weekend?"

"It's allowed now for people to visit each other?"

"Honey, does it matter? This virus is a sham. Your father's cousin got it and lost his taste. Although with the girls he picks up, I'd say he can't blame the virus."

"My roommate keeps talking about how this virus has killed thousands. And—"

"Do we have insurance? Yes. Can we get into a private hospital? Also yes. Are you healthy? Yes. What's the problem? If anything, it gave your father a good excuse to start focusing on the investment allocations in his portfolio, and so far they're doing well. Hopefully, that will put our finances in a position where your uncle will be tickled pink and unfreeze your inheritance."

"Wait, where are we with that?" Olivia kept picking at the stray piece of dead skin at the corner of her nail she couldn't seem to pluck off. Annoyed, she began to gnaw on it as her mother took her time to respond.

"Um, your father is there now and trying to get it resolved, I think."

"In London?"

"Yes, Olivia. I just said that. Anyway, stop worrying so much about it. Worst case, you come back here. Your father diversifies his portfolio. Though he is heavily in entertainment and hospitality as of late. He swears it's going to make a killing once the government officially drops the guardrails."

"Mom, I don't want to go back. I like not having anyone know me here, but I also don't want to worry I'll be homeless."

"If you keep worrying, you'll get COVID. So stop. Your father is taking care of it. And again, no one cares. Caroline has moved on to bigger and better things and didn't hide away. Guilty people don't hide."

Olivia scoffed. "Or they hide in plain sight knowing nothing will happen to them when they've found someone to do their dirty work."

"I hope you don't plan to talk to her that way when you come visit. Caroline is still part of the family—her family has known ours since before your poppy moved from Italy. The only thing heavier than gold is your connections. I refuse to have you tarnish it over a silly miscommunication."

At that, Olivia had to hang up. She threw her phone across the room.

How dare she? Olivia let her tears ruin her makeup, tracing the angles of her face with black ink. She didn't bother to pick up her phone when it rang again. She knew she'd have to apologize and fake an excuse of why the call dropped.

She sat in the center of the bed, facing a large window that carried so much light into the room. It was facing the now closed pool and jacuzzi. She felt anger brimming, just underneath the surface. She could hear Priscila's laughter filter into her quiet room.

Somehow that irked her more.

Trying to brush it off, Olivia got up and picked up her phone. It definitely would need to be replaced. And luckily she memorized her father's black card credentials.

Her mother had sent her a message:

3:42 p.m. You need to get your phone checked. It's dropping all of the time.

3:48 p.m.: Thirty Easy Keto Recipes for Instant Results!

Olivia dry-laughed. She felt her chest heave again, but now it came out a tremble. Unable to stop herself, Olivia grabbed her keys, mask, and headphones before running out the door. She needed to run to clear her mind. But her mother's voice continued to fill her head.

Every. Fucking. Time.

***

Every. Fucking. Time.

It drove her insane.

Every time she got home, Priscila made her fucking do it: sanitize her hands and wipe down the doorknob from both sides.

Olivia was tempted to lick the fucking doorknob just to see Priscila freak out. She satisfied her urges by slamming the door and going to her room. Priscila probably was talking to that blonde chick again, heard Olivia arriving home, ran over to the entrance, and used disinfectant wipes on the door handles and anything else Priscila suspected her to have touched. She would run back to her computer, apologize to her "bestie," and send her a text later that day asking Olivia to use hand sanitizer.

Olivia didn't even bother trying to appease her roommate anymore. In her mind, the virus was over. It had to be. She wasn't going to suffocate or join Priscila's pitiful existence by staying home and letting herself be smothered by her fears. If Olivia's parents weren't worried about the virus, why should she?

How could she go on never leaving the apartment when she already felt bored and miserable as it was? Her friends were great, but eventually the same brunch spots, same bars, same restaurants, same breweries wore on her. Caleb was... an interesting distraction, but even that began to blend in with everything else in her life. Even the time alone in nature felt tasteless: endless red desert sands and cacti weren't so poetic as when she first saw them. Her followers thought the same way; every day, her engagement numbers on Instagram and her follower count on Social Blade dropped. The lack of curated content, zero funds to expand her platform, BLM protests, and general judgment for traveling were busting her numbers.

Why was she here?

With her hair tied up and under a shower cap, she took a shower and continued to contemplate her options:

1. Go back to New York and facing the humiliation and criticism, or

2. Stay here and double down on building her brand.

In her robe and silk pajama set, she walked over to the kitchen with the intention to grab her pint of low-fat ice cream and return to her room. She couldn't help but side-eye the cookies Priscila was checking on and take her roommate's appearance into account.

It was obvious Priscila was getting the "COVID twenty," and it was settling into her thighs. Her hair was in one messy French braid. The past few weeks had dismantled Priscila's motivation on anything that wasn't related to the clinic, and that meant the crown of braids slowly disassembled into one bunched up braid with knotted ends. Her typically sharp tiny chin was a bit less defined, but it didn't take away from her beautiful light brown, almond-shaped eyes. She was in an old college t-shirt and boy shorts. And clearly struggling to reach the frosting tips at the top of the cabinet. (In classic Priscila fashion, she never bothered to ask anyone for help and thus nearly fell while climbing down from the counter.)

Olivia shook her head and made a face; she wasn't much taller than her clumsy roommate, but she didn't need to do parkour to reach any ingredients. She could have helped but wouldn't unless Priscila sucked it up and asked for it.

Priscila turned around and made eye contact with Olivia.

"Hey."

"Hey."

Olivia moved to grab a large glass of water when Priscila cleared her throat. Then:

"How's your day going?"

"Not bad. Could be better." Olivia was almost done filling up her glass of water from the filtered sink faucet.

"That sucks… How's Connor doing?"

Olivia smiled a bit, her back still toward Priscila.

"You mean Caleb? It's… fun. Yeah, it's fun I guess." Olivia turned around and leaned against the sink as she took a sip of water.

Priscila quirked her head. "I thought you guys were pretty serious. I mean, he's on your stories a lot."

Olivia smiled a bit bigger. "I'm not with anyone until they're on the grid. That makes anyone Instagram official. This is more of a situation-ship."

Priscila laughed. "I've never heard that term before, but I see what you mean. Game recognizes game. If he wants to lock it in, he has to put in the work."

Olivia nodded and took another sip of water.

"Oh, by the way, I probably made too many cookies. Do you want to try one? I'm supposed to wait for them to cool off before adding the frosting, but they're red velvet—I don't have the patience for that."

Olivia hesitated, but picked up the one with the fewest white chocolate chip chunks. As her lips touched the warm, chocolatey surface, she couldn't help but to close her eyes.

"I can't tell if you're enjoying it or if you're figuring out how to tell me they suck."

Olivia shook her head and tried to swallow the piece she had bit into. "Trust me, I'd tell you if they sucked. These are really good. But I'll do you one better: add a scoop of vanilla ice cream."

Priscila tapped her nose and moved to the freezer. "Yeah, I only have coffee and green tea ice cream."

Olivia grabbed two plates and scooped from her own pint of vanilla bean ice cream. "It's okay—I have some. And it's low-fat." As they prepared their desserts, Priscila sighed and took a bite of her ice cream sandwich.

Olivia covered her mouth with her hand in between bites. "How are things going on your end? How's the clinic?" Priscila put her sandwich down with a sad look. "Well, cases are climbing, and my family won't let me visit. Luckily, I can fix most of the computer issues remotely. I've also been applying and hearing back from companies, but... this is just such an unprecedented time."

"Is your brother okay?" Olivia figured Vincent would likely face more of the same discrimination in Arizona as he did in Seattle, as unfortunate as that was.

"He and my mom are fine, but she has to go into the office since she works for the government." Priscila shook her head. "Vincent told me a lot of the patients don't have access to Wi-Fi or can't figure out how to use the clinic's website because English isn't their first language. So I'm basically duplicating the site in Spanish, and Vincent is helping me translate the site in Mandarin after his shifts.

"But honestly, I didn't realize how basic things like access to Wi-Fi impacted healthcare. I know I grew up privileged—I was one of the few nonwhite people in Tanque Verde—but the lack of healthcare services really opened my eyes... and yet, is it bad I'm still sad? I'm obviously sad this is happening and they are suffering and getting zero help. There's so many immigrants in Tucson without access to healthcare. But I'm also sad I'm stuck here. I could go to work for another company and eventually go to France and retire and forget them. And I feel guilty I still want to do that, because it's hard knowing they're not all going to make it through this year. It's depressing. I feel like shit knowing I'm lucky my parents are wealthy and educated and immigrated here without issues. And I still want to—just ignore everything..." Priscila stood over the granite table. "I'm a shitty person. I really have nothing to worry about, and yet I feel like shit for dreaming of Paris."

Olivia watched Priscila deflate. "Priscila, you're human. This is hard on all of us. We're angry and sad and frustrated. We're literally a petri dish waiting for this virus to engage with us. I think it's fair we still want to escape. Hell, being cut off by my parents because my stupid uncle is lawyering up on the inheritance that was allocated to me is fucking damaging. I don't rely on that money, but fuck, I'm scared not having that safety net. I can't work on my brand, something that could become into a business! I want to do all these things and I'm being forced to pause my life!"

Olivia felt her heart race. "This isn't what any of us pictured our lives to look like. This fucking virus is less of a virus and more like a whip the government wants to use to fuck with us. Everything is tanking. It's all—"

"Fuckery. It's fuckery." Priscila tried to smile but her mouth looked more like a grim line.

Olivia rubbed the back of her head, feeling the tension of the neat ponytail pulling at her last nerve. Seeing Priscila savoring every bite of the cookie slowly and carefully while Olivia devoted most of her bites to the ice cream snapped the last of her reserve like a rubber band. "Fuck it," she said, tearing the scrunchy off her ponytail, grabbing another cookie, and taking a large bite. "Tonight feels like an ice cream, cookies, and Disney-Plus kind of night. What do you think?"

Priscila smiled and leaned on the opposite end of the granite countertop. "I'll make White Russians if you pick the movie."

***

Here's the thing, when people are disappointed with the government, audiences thirst for heroes who come from the ashes and inspire change.

That was the goal.

Hamilton was an incredible piece of artistry: it intertwined the immigrant ideal of the American Dream and contained a diverse selection of actors. Throw in some rap, and you get a piece of beauty.

And yet, it was 11:30 p.m., and Olivia and Priscila were still arguing.

"You can't say this is based off of a biography of a historical figure and not assume the audience will interpret it as a musical based on the book!" Priscila had been "not yelling" for the past hour on the same point.

"Broadway isn't a history book though. If people wanted to actually learn about Alexander Hamilton without the catchy lyrics, they should read the book." Olivia didn't care her slow speech would come off as demeaning. She was tired of going in circles.

Priscila was clearly indignant. "Not everyone is going to take the time to read more about the figure! And it's one thing to take artistic freedoms, but it's another to sidestep an entire piece of history and not try to address the clear racism of that time."

The White Russians were starting to hit Olivia pretty hard, but she continued to top off of her current drink with the last of the Bailey's. Olivia took a sip before giving Priscila a deadpan look. "Honestly, that's not Lin-Manuel's problem; that's a much larger problem than the artist intended to engage with. And I would think you'd be happy to see amazing actors who have become famous because of this, by the way, instead of criticizing they were there to begin with."

Priscila had long ago abandoned her drink and half-eaten red velvet cookie.

"I'm glad he is producing work that's centered on inclusion, but for fuck's sake, you can't have a slave-owning founding father played by a Black actor. It doesn't correct the massive issue. It makes it look like now you've added color to theatre, the reparation is done." Priscila's words tumbled out of her, tripping over her next sentence as she continued to "speak." "It's like the Aunt Jemima image—reparations go beyond 'inclusion.' Having based an entire product line branded with forgotten stereotypes isn't being inclusive. This is not the same as branding Madam C.J. Walker hair products that were actually developed and owned by a Black woman. You have to look at the historical context on how art and brands are produced."

Olivia wanted to throw her hands in the air but tried to instead nurse her drink.

"I'm not saying the historical context isn't important. I'm saying it's not fair to drop that on the creators—"

"Olivia, history is everything. This shit we are living through is like living on top of corpses. And the problem is, people think the corpses are buried more than six feet under. But the sediment is loosening up, and the evidence we are standing not that far away from these injustices is so clear. We're either excavating for the truth or standing on the grave."

Olivia slammed her drink, slipping alcohol onto the table. "Okay, so what does this have to do with the musical? So we're not supposed to see it because it's not designed the way you want it to look? And what do you want these 'audiences' to do? Hate themselves for being products of this shit that happened before they were born? My dad didn't come here and build a business without working. My Sicilian great-grandparents didn't have a warm welcome either. So I need to pay a penance for something my family didn't even do? That I didn't do? I don't understand how this makes me— an audience member supporting a Latino director—evil."

"I'm not saying that!"

"You are! You so are! Yes, I'm lucky I have what I have, but my parents and I work hard to continue to do well! And we're supporting others by paying for their services and productions."

"Congratulations, Olivia, but so do my parents!"

Olivia's eyes felt like they were going to fall out of her skull. "Exactly! We both benefit from the same system. We both grew up going to great schools. Our parents and ancestors immigrated to the US for a better life and did well. We are pursuing our dreams and working hard at it. But because I'm White, I'm now part of the problem? For fuck's sake, I probably lost my entire retirement savings because of petty family drama. I'm so fucking middle class right now it hurts. So please explain to me how me loving Lin Manuel's work is problematic. How me raving over the internet is 'perpetuating racism.'"

Priscila took a long sip of her lukewarm drink, and lowered her voice. "Olivia, let's not kid ourselves. You are never going to compare your life with mine. Economically speaking, we both are dealing with the same things. But you weren't beaten up for being Asian like my brother. You aren't called a wetback for being Mexican like me. And words mean nothing until people feel emboldened to act on the rhetoric they've been told is okay to say and let out their frus- tration on the scapegoats. Oh, but please tell me how being Italian-American or second-generation British has negatively impacted your applications!"

Olivia tried to counter, but Priscila continued on, her glare set on Olivia.

"But you aren't persecuted for your sexuality, your faith, or your appearance. I'm not going to pretend I face it all that much anymore; I'm *privileged* in that I'm ethnically ambiguous. White-passing, if you will. But most people don't have that. And I'm not saying you need to martyr yourself, but if these musicals are making you believe because you see a Black man holding hands with a Latino on stage with a predominately wealthy White audience yet you haven't benefited from the systems in place, you've only proven my point. Things are *not* okay—they are so far away from equal it's laughable."

Still sitting at adjacent ends of the couch, Olivia all but yelled at Priscila.

"Do you think I still don't face attacks? Do you fucking know what it feels like to know you can't go back home without being criticized? Because for someone who seems to have so many disadvantages, you seem to be handling this isolation perfectly well! Your family, your best friend, your college friends, and even the local café owners seem to be checking up on you all the damn time. I fucking have no one to connect with. I have hundreds of people who hate me because I made one small mistake! I fucked up once and my whole life is destroyed and that's the only reason I moved to bum-fuck Egypt! I tried to do the right thing, and I get accused of fraud—I get destroyed over the stupidest shit."

Olivia got up and started to move away, not willing to explain further. But Priscila wasn't prepared to let her do that. With crossed arms, Priscila moved to block Olivia's way out of the living room.

"What the hell did you do in New York? Why are you here?"

Olivia felt a tingle climb up her right arm and over her chest.

"Fuck off, Priscila."

"Olivia, you live here under a sublease. I need to know if you are doing illegal shit that's going to bite me in the ass later. I will call the landlord to do a background check."

Olivia felt that static feeling spread further up to her neck. And as much as she would love to flip off Priscila and leave, she had nowhere to go. She couldn't go back to New York. Not yet. She needed to rebuild before going back. And with COVID destroying New York, she really didn't have anywhere else to go.

She decided to come clean. "I was accused of funneling some money out of a non-profit I was working with. Because I trusted family friends on a joint venture and signed paperwork without reading. But my name was cleared. Now, get the fuck out of the way."

***

Paige and Morgan were nice enough to offer their apartments, but Olivia knew she couldn't keep avoiding Priscila. Between contractually being obligated to stay at her apartment until December 31 and lacking funds to make such a big move, she was, yet again, stuck.

Olivia mindlessly counted the air bubbles on Paige's living room ceiling, waiting for her to return with some dip. Morgan had gone out for alcohol since her "crazy bitch of a roommate" needed "to be canceled out with wine." It had already been a week, and Priscila still hadn't apologized or made any move to remedy the situation. Olivia couldn't keep doing this.

She needed to leave.

When Morgan got back, Paige and Olivia were half-way through planning the Grand Canyon trip with a few of Paige's sorority sisters and Morgan's high school friends. And of course, Caleb was one text away from joining the fun.

Olivia needed to leave. Priscila be damned.

BELEN, LOS ANGELES— AUGUST 2020

She didn't think it would take all of twenty minutes to have this conversation. She thought she would check in for ten minutes and they would talk about the great marks she received for her classes, mention she needed her official transcript for her LSE application, and wrap up. She wasn't expecting the call to go this way though.

It was five minutes after the hour and her dean still wasn't on the call. As she waited, she continued to fill out Axel's class schedule and read the supplement information about school services that would be continued online.

With nearly eighteen minutes left of the original thirty-minute call, Belen was startled to hear the crackled start of the video chat.

"Hi, Belen, apologies on the tardiness. I have had consecutive calls for the past hour and a half and needed to run to the restroom for a second. Give me a moment to pull up your student account."

"Of course. No worries." Belen grabbed her notebook and turned to her bookmarked page as she heard her dean patter on the keyboard to search for her name.

"Okay. Well, it looks like you're on way to graduation. All of your study abroad credits from LSE transferred over without a hitch. Congratulations on the high marks by the way—it's very impressive to keep such a high GPA during a study abroad program, especially in these unprecedented times."

"Thank you. I'm actually looking to apply to LSE for graduate school, so I was hoping to get my official transcript sent to my home address."

"Hm. Cutting it close there with the end of your undergraduate program to jump across the pond to the graduate program, no?" The Zoom call garbled some of the dean's words.

"I'm sorry, can you say that again? I couldn't understand you—poor reception." Belen moved to the living room, hoping Axel wouldn't try to distract her as she tried to get the audio connection stronger. She decided to turn off her video feed, and suddenly the audio poured out of her Mac.

"—you are going to need to show you are graduating before their September 2021 start date. Can you hear me now?" Her dean's glasses slipped to the tip of her nose as she seemingly tried to adjust the settings of her computer.

"I can hear you now. Sorry, can you repeat that again? I have seen other students go directly from their undergrad to a master's program." She plugged in her earphones and raised the volume of her computer.

"Right, but what I'm saying is you won't be hitting the final requirements until Summer 2021. You'll need to check if they'll allow that."

This jolted Belen, and her voice climbed an octave.

"What do you mean Summer 2021? You mean a June graduation, correct?"

"No. August 2021... you're missing your ethnics studies requirements. Can you see my screen?"

Her screen shared an electronic system that marked in red the two courses that would set her off track and push the finish line further back.

"But I fulfilled the ethnics requirements. They were about Jewish migrations across the nineteenth century! It was literally one of the first classes I took! If you look at my course history list, you'll see that it's—"

The dean's tone turned terse: "You need to work with the department head about this. I can't override it without their written consent. We've run out of time, but you can schedule another call with my calendar link, available in my signature line. If you need anything else, write me over email... I'll send you the official transcript next week."

Belen felt her heart rate in her eardrums as she watched the screen turn black.

"Fuck. Fuck, fuck, fuck—" Belen held her breath before releasing a teary, "Fuck!"

Belen jammed her fingers against her keyboard, searching for the head of the ethnic studies department. The fury radiated from her—to the point Axel cautiously walked around her seat in the living room to use the bathroom. After he was done, he lingered near the wall of the living room, pulling at a stray thread.

"Belen, I have a meeting with my guidance counselor. Can you set it up?"

"Ugh, just give—I'm sorry, I'm just finding out something and I'm a little frustrated. Just give me a second." She kept her back to him; however, after feeling him hover behind her, she sighed and turned to him. "What's up? "

"I don't know what to do for the meeting." Axel continued to look at his toes, stretching the stray thread so it bunched the corner of his shirt.

Belen swatted his hand from the offending thread. "Nothing. It'll be casual. But I do need to read some information before speaking to Ms. Garcia about your classes so we can figure it out together."

"Will I get to stay home?" Axel pet the shirt again, eventually moving to smooth it over.

"Yeah, you'll still be home for a while. But maybe we will get to have you speak to Ms. Cynthia a few times a week. Do you remember the lady we met a few months ago? She was really nice." Belen turned back to glance at her emails, hoping to see a note from her Dean.

"I would rather not talk to her." Axel started to pull at the thread again.

Belen looked over her shoulder and frowned. "She seemed nice. Why don't you want to talk to her?"

He didn't respond. The thread had snapped. Without having anything to entertain his hands, Axel flapped his hands with progressively more aggression. Concerned, Belen held Axel in a tight embrace and slowly rubbed small swirls on this back.

"I don't know! I just don't want to talk to her."

"Axel, would you be willing to do me a favor?" Belen asked, maintaining constant pressure on Axel's stimming body. "I don't know if I want Ms. Cynthia to be my friend, but I would like to find out if she is someone I can talk to. I trust you so much, and if you tell me she's someone I shouldn't talk to, I'll listen to you."

Axel had latched onto Belen's split ends and the coarseness of her hair propelled him to braid it.

"There is no need for you to lie to me anymore—I know you want me to give her a chance."

"Will you do it then? At least just a few meetings. Then I'll drop it."

He grunted and let go of her.

"Whatever. 'I'm fucking miserable. I had to get up at ten o'clock this morning.'"

"Axel! Language!"

"You and mom cuss all the time."

"It's different. Tu no podrías soportar una golpiza.[36] Big words come with big consequences."

"Didn't you get beat up in school? And anyway, I just need help talking to my counselor. It's almost time."

At the realization she was a minute away from the call time, Belen joined the Zoom meeting and pulled out a list of potential classes. At 10:02 a.m., Belen was greeted with Ms. Garcia's face.

"Hi, Ms. Garcia! I'm so sorry to join late—technical difficulties."

Her strained laughter was met with a warm smile. "We're all still getting used to this setup—don't worry."

"I'm Belen, and this is my baby brother, Axel. I'll be helping him with class registration."

"Oh, okay. Are you his guardian?"

"Yes! Well, no. My mother is, but I help him with classes while she's out and will be his secondary emergency contact."

"That's fine. Okay, let's get started."

---

36 Translation: You wouldn't be able to handle a punch.

***

While Axel tended to the garden, Belen redirected her attention to her "unfulfilled" ethnics requirement. She had written half of her message when her mother arose from her bedroom and joined Belen in the living room. Immediately, Belen closed her laptop and handed her mother a water bottle and her medication.

"¿Y la junta?[37] How did it go?"

Her mother's voice was hoarse, and her eyes were bloodshot.

"Axel is signed up for the normal classes and won't be placed with the special needs students. He'll have biweekly calls with the social therapist we met last year, Ms. Cynthia."

"She was nice."

"It'll be good for him. He doesn't have friends, and he's been acting out."

Immediately, she regretted saying anything at all.

"What did he say this time? ¿Anda de malcriado otra vez?[38]"

"No. He's just quoting this movie that says inappropriate words, but I've already talked to him about it." Belen continued quickly before her mother could cut her off again. "And I'll add some restrictions on his phone so he's not seeing anything too mature. Don't worry."

Her mother sighed and sank a bit more into the seat. "How about you? How did your meeting go?"

"Fine. We just discussed what I should plan to take for the next few semesters. I'm all on track."

---

37 Translation: And the meeting?
38 Translation: Is he being disrespectful again?

Belen instantly regretted her last sentence.

"I'm so proud of you. I pray this pandemic is over so I can show off my beautiful daughter with her UCSD degree. All of the long days are worth it. For both of you."

Her mother radiated pride and her eyes shined a bit more before the lucidness disappeared.

"Mija,[39] I'm sorry, but I need to sleep a bit more before my shift—"

"Don't worry. I understand. Do you want me to turn off the lights?"

"No. I need to get up in a few minutes, but I just want to rest my eyes."

"Okay."

Belen walked over and grabbed the pink blanket next to the futon. She tucked her mom in and waved away her mom's small protests to leave her be. She continued to tuck her in until she felt cold blistered feet rub against her hands. She paused and felt her eyes swell. She lightly sat on the floor and rubbed her mom's feet until they warmed. Her mother's snores didn't stop her from massaging her feet.

Her mind kept rewinding her dean's voice, and her fear deepened. What if she couldn't graduate? She already had so much collecting in student loans. And what about walking? She figured it wasn't possible this year, with the pandemic, but she had been looking forward to a formal ceremony since she started her classes at UCSD. Would she have to wait until the following year? And if LSE didn't accept her late graduation—could she even get in? She couldn't fathom looking for a job in this economy. Especially when she didn't even major in STEM. She felt her throat tighten and pain

---

39 Translation: shortened form of "my daughter"

behind her eyes. Her chest felt like it was about to collapse into itself.

She quietly moved her mother's feet onto the couch and tucked them into the blanket. Belen's feet barely touched the floor as she lightly scurried across the room. She grabbed her laptop and charger and moved into her room. Locking it, she grabbed her noise cancelling headphones and blasted music to silence the troubling doubts in her mind. She knew if she let them sing too long, they would have an orchestra resounding the same tune. Even as she finished and sent the message to the Head of Ethnic Studies Department, she felt shaken. She grabbed her Virgin Mary of Guadalupe candle and read the prayer listed on the back. Her white knuckles clutched the candle as if it was the only thing that kept her from flying away. As she lit the candle, she felt a bit better and grabbed her laptop once again.

She might not have answers, but she was excellent at research and organization. She began to investigate LSE's portal on graduate degrees and occasionally glanced at the glowing light at the end of the room that accompanied her for hours into her research, unaware of the screaming match Axel and her mother had entered.

Fall 2020

As doctors worry about 'a very apocalyptic fall,' the CDC retracts info on how Covid-19 spreads.

OCT. 1
N.Y.C. was the first major U.S. city to reopen all its public schools for in-person learning.

SEPT. 3
The virus surged at U.S. colleges, totaling more than 51,000 cases.

NOV. 13
The C.D.C. said children's visits to the emergency room for mental health had risen.

OCT. 24
Poland's president tested positive.

SEPT. 22
The U.S. death toll surpassed 200,000.

OCT. 2
President Trump tested positive for the virus.

NOV. 17
F.D.A. authorized the first at-home coronavirus test.

NOV. 5
Coronavirus cases

U.S. colleges hit a quarter mi

SEPT. 28
Global deaths reached 1 million

Total US Confirmed COVID-19 Cases on September 20th, 2020: 6,825,949
Death Count on September 20th, 2020: 199,267

OCT. 11
The world recorded more than 1 million new cases in three days.

NOV. 18
The U.S. death toll hit 250,000.

SEPT. 13
The Midwest

SEPT. 18
Israel imposed a second national lockdown.

NOV. 6
England entered a national lockdown.

NOV. 21
The F.D.A. granted emergency authorization of the coronavirus antibody treatment given to President Trump

NOV. 8
The U.S. surpassed 10 million infections.

SEPT. 6
India became the country with the second-highest number of cases with more than 4 million.

LEILANI, EMERYVILLE— SEPTEMBER 2020

———

Michael kissed the top of Leilani's head as she applied a bit more blush. He looked at Leilani through the mirror and smiled.

"You look beautiful. And the house is spotless. So can you please chill? I don't think the call will be more than fifteen minutes. My little cousin isn't even joining the call."

Leilani rolled her eyes and adjusted the coffee table once more before checking her reflection one last time. She wanted to make sure her nude lipstick hadn't smeared onto her just-whitened teeth. She combed through her hair again, adjusting the bouncing flat, ironed curls. She knew what her sisters would say. She knew what her friends would say.

Hell, she hated herself for doing it; the anxiety of hiding Michael made her tense her throat, fearing her own voice.

She rubbed her neck and took a deep breath. Leilani grabbed her phone, opened her "Notes" section on her phone, and recited her mantras mentally:

I am conquering my fears and becoming stronger each day.

I will have a good day because it's my choice.

I am not afraid of other's thoughts about me because I
am en—

Her brown skin wasn't going anywhere. And though Michael's pasty skin had splotches of red and light fawn beige, it didn't hide the fact he passed for White.

She never had this experience before with any other boyfriend—willingly committing herself into a prolonged observation in the petri dish she called her apartment. Michael's fidgeting hands told her he, at least subconsciously, recognized they were in for a stressful evening.

Out of her peripheral vision, Leilani caught Michael using his dress pants to wipe down his sweaty palms yet again.

"Are you ready?" Michael wrapped his arms around her and nested his head in the crook of her neck. She watched their reflection as she held onto his noodle-like arms.

She smiled at him. "Let's do it."

But the confidence in her voice seemed to die when they hit the thirty-minute mark of their video call. Michael's little sister, Joanna, luckily carried most of the conversation. Joanna had the same wide hazel eyes Michael had with dusty brown hair placed into a neat bun, making her look a bit older than she was. Her conversations rounded her back to her actual age—at sixteen years old, she clearly enjoyed torturing Michael with embarrassing anecdotes from their childhood.

Michael's mother enthusiastically added more color to the stories. Her warm smile offered Leilani some comfort, but she didn't offer any information about herself. Michael's aunt seemed more willing to share, though she didn't mention her child, the cousin Michael talked about so often.

Leilani refused to lose the few supporters she had. Despite the small fits of laughter Joanna coaxed from her family and Leilani, Michael's father was less than entertained. His tight smile made Leilani's urge to fiddle with her skirt unbearable.

But she continued to look straight at his image on her screen. In a dark blue button-up, he was an unmoving force in the call. Michael was impossible to anger, but his resemblance to his father made Leilani stare down a "would-be" older Michael, judging her with contempt. The familiar cross Leilani grew up with hung behind Michael's father, appearing more menacing with the tribunal of other saints' frames surrounding it.

Michael kept translating pieces of the conversation into Arabic for his aunt. She seemed to follow what she could in English but appeared grateful for the clarification. But while Leilani waited for Michael to finish translating, her eyes drifted toward the portrait of the pale, older man with a tight lip looking down on her. Michael's father squinted as if to get a better look at her, with sunburnt skin, slight redden and tan, but never the less White.

Leilani readjusted the skirt of her dress again.

"Charbel, do you have any questions for Leilani? You're so quiet. Why can't you act like this when I am watching my shows?" Mrs. Boutros nudged her husband who shook his head and readjusted his position on the couch, surrounded by his female relatives.

"So." He readjusted his posture, clearly tired. "Our son, Michael, is very important to us. He makes us very proud and he's a great boy—" he cleared his throat and corrected himself "—a good man. What does your family say about you two?"

This was one of the questions Leilani feared—she had even avoided the subject with Michael. Out of the corner of her eye, she saw Michael grip his knee.

She took a slow breath to look at Michael, who gave her a nervous look. Leilani smiled at him as she crossed her ankles.

"I am actually trying to figure out when to..." She couldn't hold Michael's gaze. "When to introduce him formally to my family. My father was recovering from a heart attack, but once he's doing better..." Leilani stared at the St. Charbel image, "I plan to introduce them."

"Oh, they don't know about you two?" Joanna cocked her head to the side, scrunching her eyebrows together.

"Well, they'd want a formal introduction, just as I am doing with you all." Leilani felt her hand sweating through the fabric of her dress.

"Hmm. A proper introduction makes sense." Luckily, Michael's mother continued to nod as she waited for Michael to finish translating for his aunt. He paused and looked at Leilani before responding with his aunt's words. Eventually, Michael's aunt gave an odd face and half shrug. Michael's father pursed his lips and did not say anything else.

He did not speak for another hour. Ms. Boutros would attempt to engage him in the conversation, but he would ask information about her family before dropping the subject as Leilani gave vague answers. Joanna and Michael's aunt asked what everyone had done during the pandemic, and they shared more stories about Michael. Mrs. Boutros would occasionally throw a look at Mr. Boutros, to no avail.

"Charbel, do you want to say anything? It's getting late and you just sit there." Mr. Boutros sucked his teeth and slumped a bit back in the chair, fixing his posture.

"Okay, Marie. Okay." He leaned on one of the arm rests. "Leilani, tell us about your parents. Are they religious?"

Leilani eyed the rosary on Michael's wrist. He must have felt her gaze as he moved his hand gently onto her knee, out of frame of the laptop's camera.

"Um, well… I grew up Christian, but my mother was the more religious one, and she left us when I was very young. My father raised us, but my sisters took me to church when he picked up extra shifts."

Charbel raised an eyebrow. "So you are a practicing Christian?"

Leilani tightly fisted her hand, digging her nails into her fleshy palms. Michael's hold on her knee tightened. Leilani couldn't risk looking at Michael and pushed through. "I believe in God, though I'm still trying to figure out Christianity. But my family is still very religious."

Mr. Boutros looked unconvinced.

"But she pushes me to do my days of obligation, knowing Oum[40] will be upset if I don't." Michael added quickly, holding Leilani closer to him, slightly engulfing her frame. He looked at her and smiled. "She definitely makes sure I'm being true to myself and I don't forget to come back to my roots."

Leilani couldn't help but to smile back.

"How old were you when she left?" Joanna prodded as only a sixteen-year-old could.

"Joanna!" In a slew of Arabic, Mrs. Boutros simultaneously scolded Joanna while updating her sister-in-law in the conversation. Michael's aunt looked at each of her family members, throwing in a few choice words in Arabic to her niece and brother before her eyes landed on Leilani. She smiled tightly but didn't say anything else.

---

40 Translation: [connotation of high respect and admiration] Mother

"I've never seen her again. She lives with her new family in Upstate New York, I'm told, with the man she left my father for."

Joanna couldn't contain herself, as much as Leilani wished her to. "Haven't you ever been curious to why she left, or what your half siblings—ouch!"

Mrs. Boutros replied in Arabic to her daughter, who rubbed her arm from an off-screen pinch.

Hesitant but needing to justify herself, Leilani took a breath. "She married my father because she was told to—she never intended on staying with him so long. She..." Leilani took a deep breath, "wanted to make it easier for her new husband by not bringing her family along for the ride. There are five of us. We're a bit hard to manage."

They didn't fit in her mother's dream.

"But Leilani's father is extremely hard working and raised his girls to be strong, independent women." Michael squeezed Leilani's shoulders. "And just look at her—she has a full ride to UC Berkeley and is working at a notable corporate law firm. Not everyone can do that."

"Is your company hiring any remote interns by chance, Leilani? I'd love to learn more about working in a law firm." Joanna was unfazed by her mother's eye roll.

"Of course. I'll get your email address from Michael and refer you." Leilani couldn't help but to smile at Joanna's triumphant fist pump.

"And with that, I think Leilani and I should get going on preparing our dinner—at this rate, we won't eat until midnight!" Michael shifted forward, taking up practically the entire video feed.

"It is late. Enjoy your evening, Michael. We need to head over to our outdoor mass soon. Say goodbye to your Auntie

Leyla." Michael began to say his goodbyes in Arabic, and his aunt nodded, her short, wavy brunette hair bouncing around her shoulders.

Eventually, Michael closed the laptop.

He slumped back onto the couch. "See? That wasn't too bad."

Leilani laid on his arm and hummed, but her heart rate accelerated. She hoped he would forget about meeting her family.

"So when are you thinking of introducing me to your father?"

Shit.

OLIVIA, SCOTTSDALE—
SEPTEMBER 2020

———

Olivia tried not to feel guilty. As she prepared her next few posts, she tried to think through a short list of people to interview in a live video chat, but her mind wandered. She forced herself to stay away from the kitchen and keep from eating all of her pumpkin cupcakes.

And the more she tried not to think about the thick, buttercream frosting or the cinnamon topped dusting on sweet pumpkin bread, the more she salivated. She didn't blame Priscila for eating her weight in sweets—she just blamed her for making her do the same thing. And it was this train of thought that caused her to feel alone. Because if she told anyone how she actually felt, what she actually thought, she would be judged for "fat shaming."

She knew from Priscila's texts she was going to have a rough time when she had gotten back from the Grand Canyon. But she couldn't make herself care. Priscila acted like she was her parent when she was only three years older.

It was ten days later, and she was still not showing symptoms. Clearly, Priscila was blowing this out of proportion. Again. Like the fucking clinic. She felt bad people were struggling, but Priscila had to realize Olivia can't lose herself to be a solution for others. It was a shitty situation, but it's unrealistic to assume people will always give up everything for a friend. Or Priscila should do it. Or if she was going to do it, everyone else had to follow in her footsteps.

Plus, Olivia *was* helping others.

After crying her eyes out on a livestream, the outpour of fans and supporters finally lifted Olivia out of a depression. People who were also frustrated encouraged her to reconnect with nature. And they mentioned how they loved her posts.

People escaped with her. They adored her raw honesty; her rough and broken edges. Her supporters became her friends and family—and Priscila wasn't going to take that away from her.

Olivia sighed. She shouldn't feel guilty for reaching for a cupcake either. Or blame Priscila for using desserts as a coping mechanism.

And it's *one* cupcake—it wasn't going to kill her.

Olivia moved out of her room, nearly tripping on the pile of clean but unfolded laundry next to her bed. Though the kitchen looked empty, Olivia realized Priscila was on the same nook of the couch as always but now with an oversized sweater, a loose hair bun, and a cup of coffee.

Olivia watched Priscila, who in turn slightly acknowledged her presence by shifting in her seat and nesting further into the couch. Olivia rolled her eyes and found the baker's dozen of cupcakes on the counter. Unable to stop herself, she opened the lid and took a bite out of one with the lightest amount of frosting. The richness of the cupcake traveled through her lazy smile and quieted her growling stomach. She took a second, larger bite that lead to a third and fourth. She knew she'd have to avoid the cute bakery on her next run—it was clearly too dangerous for her.

Before Olivia was able to reach for a glass of milk, she felt the cinnamon tickle her throat, as well as some kind of rough edge—probably a piece of a walnut. Her fit of coughs lasted maybe fifteen seconds, but it was all it took for Priscila to freak out and open a window. Not satisfied with her own performance of disapproval, Priscila took her work to the balcony despite the heat of the evening, clearly unwilling to breathe the same air as Olivia.

Olivia took another bite after pouring herself a glass of milk, riled up with anger and inspired to continue her interviews.

***

Though it seemed Arizona was still relatively hot in late September, that day was a bit chillier than expected.

Olivia blamed it on global warming. Priscila probably blamed it on her.

Olivia had been texting Steven, her Grand Canyon fling, and was preparing a small cooler to finally join him pool-side at his apartment complex. She packed mini bottles of champagne and strawberries while she considered her luck in having Caleb flake on the trip at the last minute. Steven and Olivia had hit it off and were now celebrating the end of their quarantine with a date. When she grabbed her spare blanket from the living room, she noticed how cold the apartment was. And though all the windows were closed, the air conditioning was on high.

Priscila sat near the air conditioner, sitting hunched over her laptop and second monitor, looking a bit like a troll. She had let her frizzy hair down—that and the dark bags under her eyes didn't help her overall appearance.

As Olivia approached the air conditioner, Priscila snapped her head up. "Don't touch it."

"Hell must have frozen over and landed here. I'm turning it off—it's fucking cold." Olivia's face warmed as she tried not to snap at Priscila.

"Olivia, put on a fucking jacket. You're wearing shorts and I see that bikini strap peeking out—you can easily layer up." Priscila stared her down, raising her left eyebrow and jutting out her lower jaw.

"I wake up congested because of the air conditioning—no amount of clothing can stop that. Plus, it's cooler outside, and you're wearing fucking sweats."

Priscila wasn't backing down; she grabbed the remote control near the air conditioning. "It's breathable cotton, and I'm overheating because I'm actually working. I can see you're packing to leave to go outside, which you just said was cold. Think of it as an adjustment to what you're about to experience."

Olivia felt a fire light inside of her. No one can say she didn't fucking try with Priscila.

"Seriously, Priscila? No. That's stupid. Turn it on when I leave. I'm not fucking dealing with this shit. You're making my life a fucking living hell. It's fucking Saturday. I work. Just because I'm not clocking sixty hours a week, it doesn't mean I don't work. At least I'm actually helping people and not just by being fucking tech support and taking credit for someone's work." Olivia clicked off the air conditioning.

Priscila turned it on with the remote control. "I'm not the one gallivanting around, half naked, at some stupid fucking trip because you have an incessant need for attention. Getting laid was *clearly* more important to you than putting my health and the entire clinic at risk. Sorry, Queen Olivia— didn't realize I was getting in your way toward finally hitting ten thousand followers and potentially gaining one friend."

Olivia jammed her finger on the "off" button. "Fuck you. Your bronchitis is not going to fucking kill you, but spending the rest of your life in this room will. Don't blame me because your life sucks and I actually like mine. Your family has drilled it in your head if you walk barefoot you'll be infertile, and if you walk out without covering your head in the rain you'll die from pneumonia like your Uncle Benny. That man died when your dad was ten years old, and I know about him because you won't shut the fuck up about how me leaving a window open overnight will kill you! Your hoax of a medical family will kill you. You're worrying about the PPE, the nurses, the clinic, the financials, all shit other employees in the clinic are working toward fixing—but you sit on your ass, doing nothing, and occasionally fixing broken hyperlinks on a website. You are criticizing me, but you're not doing shit either. You're feeling sick because of the work you're doing and hearing everyone's sob stories. I'm not going down that way. I'm not going to drown in anxiety with you, Priscila. So kindly go fuck yourself."

Olivia grabbed the last of her things and slammed the door. She heard the beep of the air conditioning being turned on again, and she stomped her way to the garage parking lot. No sooner had she pulled away from the apartment, in route to the nearest grocery store, she heard a few chimes come from her phone. When she found a close enough parking spot, she reached for her phone. Expecting to get a brief text from Steven on a message she sent, she noticed the growing number of texts from her "Desert Chics" group chat. In effort to mute the chat, she caught a message reading "tested positive." She scrolled up:

Paige: Fuckkk Jaime tested positive.

Morgan: Maybe he got it from his roommate?

Paige: Maybe… but he was with his gf during the trip, and she'd had body aches and a fever for days.

Morgan: Damn—I also got a text from Nate. Tested positive. Hey Olivia, did you get tested? If not, you probs should before your roommate bites your head off lol. I tested negative a few days ago but I'll retake it ASAP.

Olivia didn't bother to read the rest of the messages. She had headaches and a running nose for a few days, but had been blaming Priscila's air conditioning usage… who kept whining under her breath how overheated she was…

She had to be fine. She would have been coughing by now… right? Priscila occasionally huffed and had been ordering most of her food to be delivered to their apartment instead of cooking, but from what she heard of Priscila's calls, she just sounded stressed, sad, and tired.

Olivia sat in her car, staring ahead, unable to determine what she felt or figure out what to do. She turned off her engine and sat there for a few minutes until she received a text from Steven.

Steven: What's your ETA? Was thinking of ordering Italian.

Sitting in her car wasn't going to solve anything. Olivia gave a lengthy response to Steven and put his address into Google Maps.

Before pulling out of the parking spot, Olivia glanced at Steven's message.

Oh damn—sux about your roommate. No worries. I can order, and we can get delivery on whatever is missing.

BELEN, LOS ANGELES— SEPTEMBER 2020

———

Belen awoke to a fairly quiet morning and navigated through her lectures without scrolling through her social media accounts. Her coffee was mostly cold, but she felt fine enough to join the application review meeting with Patrick. It was early, but the admissions were on a rolling basis. Plus, she would soon need to apply to other graduate programs in the US.

Patrick's words lifted her up for a moment, making her feel like she didn't need to worry. But even his enthusiasm, the brief moment of optimism, seemed too much.

"Hey, is everything okay? You seem... a bit off." Patrick took off his glasses as he leaned back into his chair. From her computer screen, it looked like he was leaning his chair back far enough to tap the wall. It was bound to slip right out from under him.

"Yeah. Just tired, I guess." Belen straightened but didn't look at her camera.

Patrick moved his chair forward, balancing on its four legs instead of the back two. "Okay. You were just so quiet. But I hope you know if you need to talk through anything, academic or otherwise, I am here. You don't need to talk to me, but sometimes manifestation can be helpful."

Belen couldn't help but smirk. "Manifestation?"

"Sandy is really into yoga nowadays with the pandemic and all. She talks about how sharing things out loud can help manifest our dreams and fears."

"That sounds very... balanced."

Patrick looked around, seemingly searching for something to help him articulate. He gave up and refocused his attention on her. "I need to ask her, but it sounds like if you speak the enemy out loud, one of two things might happen: it either seems smaller, or someone will come help make it smaller. I'm not fully bought into this yoga... thing, but the point is, it helps to express it."

Belen smiled. "I'm okay. I'm just a bit stressed with family, friends, studying, work, and—" Belen waved her hands around, "this whole thing. I'm just a bit overwhelmed with the prospective of submitting this application and leaving all of this in the air."

"What do you mean?" Patrick leaned into the camera.

"I... I want to go to LSE more than anything. But the stress is really getting to me, and I worry if I don't apply now, I might never apply. But I'm also worried about being accepted. Because if I leave, what happens here? I am more aware of the finances now I'm home, and I just didn't realize it was this bad. I feel guilty for following my dreams when my family is struggling—especially because I know I'm going to be taking resources away from them. I mean, aren't they supposed to be comforting me as I'm applying to grad school? It's been the other way around lately."

Patrick stayed quiet. He pulled his peppered hair back, though the long hair strands still made their way forward and covered his face. He shifted his position in his chair and pulled his hair away from his eyes again.

This is what she was scared of—Patrick had been so kind in helping her she was afraid to tell him she might not even apply at the end of the day. That she had wasted his time.

"I recognize I can't help with the decision-making, nor can I share what I'd do in your place. However, if you're willing to talk about it, maybe I can ask questions that might guide you. And if you still feel confused, I can reach out to people who can talk to you about how to make this work if you want to pursue it. Selfishly, I think LSE would lose out on you if you don't at least apply. But applications are tied with money. I would ask you consider at least throwing your hat in the ring."

Belen gripped her hands together on her lap. "I'm sorry, Patrick, I didn't mean to make it sound like this was all a waste of time—"

"Oh, don't worry about that. I was able to meet you and learn more about all the great things you want to do and will do. The time is secondary. I just want you to know you have support in whatever you choose. I can cover the applications fee just to at least give you the option of considering LSE. I just want to understand where I can leverage my connections, with your consent."

Belen looked up, trying to hold back the tears that started to form. Her voice grew hoarse. "It means so much to me you're even offering to help, Patrick. If it's not too much, I would love help with getting some fees subsidized."

"I can cash app you what you need. Just send me your info. And remember, I offered. So it's not too much. Seriously, I think you need to be selected to study at LSE; it's a loss to everyone to not have you there."

"Thank you, Patrick. Seriously, again, thank you so much." Belen felt dry, unable to share with him the growing hole in her chest. It felt like her body was making space for her lungs to grab air. She tried to calm down as Patrick finished going through her application and signed off.

With the blank screen on her computer, she felt her body shake. Liquid streamed from her nose and eyes without a sound. She threw herself onto her bed, praying to her candle things could work out, life would get less complicated. She could continue to pursue her dreams without leaving anyone behind.

As her tears started to slow, she thought of the free counseling sessions Maggie had insisted her to attend. As much as she appreciated Patrick helping her with the cost, she couldn't let him carry all of the weight of her worries. Maybe Maggie had a point.

When her tears dried, she sat up and looked for the counselors who are available.

***

She was sweating. She mopped with wide sweeps that kept hitting obstacles along each swipe; the mop's tendrils slapped Axel's feet as he tried to tiptoe across the damp floor. A crass word slipped out of his mouth and was met with a glare from Belen. But the even exchange didn't slow her down. She intentionally worked around him, confining him into one spot.

"Belen, where am I supposed to stand?" Axel looked lost as he watched his sister close his laptop and move his backpack to the couch. He was surrounded by Pine-Sol scented floors with no obstacle to jump on to avoid touching the floor.

"Puchica,[41] you saw me cleaning en friega y no te moviste![42] And don't you dare step there—that's clean! I don't know how you're going to get to the living room. I asked you to move an hour ago and you didn't do anything."

"Belen, I'm not Jesus. I can't float above the ground and over to the living room." He mumbled at a lower tone. "Trust me. I have tried." Axel stayed in place as Belen continued to mop in his direction. Still she didn't waste time to look at him.

"Then why didn't you do it when I asked you to? A ver como te las arreglas, pero no te quiero allí."[43] Belen was a foot away and gripping her mop harder.

"Belen, how the fuck am I supposed to get there? I told you I had to finish my assignment!" Axel stomped over the wet floor, nearly slipping and eventually making it over to the living room.

"Que te dije? Ya viste? Pero es porque no me haces caso!"[44] Belen kept her head down and finished polishing the last bit of the tiles before wiping her rubber house slippers on the mop. She continued to apply a wood protectant on the table as she waited for part of the floor to finish drying.

"Siri, what time is it?" Belen shouted to her phone at the other end of the kitchen and dining area.

---

41 Translation: Damn
42 Translation: in a rush and you didn't move
43 Translation: Let's see how you fix it, but I don't want you there.
44 Translation: What did I say? You see? But it happened because you don't listen to me!

An "I'm sorry, I didn't get that" response was followed by a chime. Even at Belen's multiple attempts, her phone failed to understand.

"Axel, what time is it?"

"I'm sorry, I didn't get that. Please try again later."

She could scream. But hearing her mother's Toyota pull into the driveway pushed Belen to finish wiping down the table. Her mother was late, again.

"Hola, Mami." Axel jumped up and tried to say hello but not before their mom kissed both of them on the top of their heads.

"Hola, hola. Cipotes, todavía no están listo? Belen, te dije que ayudaras! Ay no, ya es tarde![45] Where's my towel?" Her mother looked like a hen without its head, flopping around to ready her children.

"It's in the bathroom! I already told him, but don't worry, I'll get him ready." Belen looked like a wreck, but she had thankfully set her clothes out earlier. She finished her work on the table and moved to Axel's room, avoiding her brother who was trying to find his pants.

"Axel, I told you to get your outfit ready last night!"

Belen started to pull at drawers and took a quick inventory of shirts he hid in the back, jumbled and wrinkled.

"I don't understand why we are getting dressed if back to school night is virtual. We could be wearing just pj's and they wouldn't care or notice."

"Axel, it's not about that. We need to make a good first impression because we'll have the virtual meeting with them next week for the Individualized Educational Plan."

---

45 Translation: Child, you're still not ready? Belen, I told you to help! Oh no, it's so late!

"It's called an IEP, Belen. And they don't care. They said so."

"We care. I don't care about everyone else. Now, use this." Belen said, handing him a wrinkle resistant, white linen button up with small green palm tree print. "You're organizing these drawers after the call. Did you finish your homework?"

Axel looked at her blankly and slowly put on the shirt. Belen knew he hated the shirt and would test her patience to not wear it. He scratched his arms as soon as the fabric touched his skin.

Belen stared him down. Axel finished putting it on. She turned around as he started to switch from his joggers to his jeans.

"I told you I needed help. You were ignoring me all morning." Axel whined.

"Axel, I *also* have school. I'm studying all morning and cleaning and cooking and trying to help *you*! What more do you want?"

Axel finished and nudged Belen he was done.

"I want to not have homework."

Belen sighed and looked up. She shook her head and stretched her back. "You know, Mom can deal with you and your homework if you'd like."

Axel tensed and shook his head.

"I thought so. Start setting up the meeting on the computer and I'll be there in a moment."

***

In thirty minutes, they put themselves together; in fifteen minutes, chaos ensued.

"Your teacher is asking you a question, Axel. Why don't you respond?" Their mother kept pushing Axel to at least pretend to care and engage with every comment the teacher gave. *And* type all of her questions.

"Mom, they don't care. They don't notice you are asking questions. They don't look at anything we're writing. This is their five-minute overview."

Their mother wasn't satisfied with the answer and shooed Axel to the side to type in her own questions. Her mother and Axel continued to bicker through the presentation.

"Belen, are you recording this on your phone? This child is making it impossible to pay attention." Her mother hogged the entire laptop screen as she chicken pecked the keyboard. The teacher continued on, even when his audio was occasionally lost or distorted.

"Mom, he's not going to answer your questions."

"Then why is there a chat box? It's so we're able to communicate with him! Change your attitude because you're really frustrating me now."

Axel sighed. Belen glared at Axel and moved to help her mother type out her questions. How her mother managed her sales job by averaging six words per minute was beyond her.

"Did you at least list us as wanting to join the two-minute introduction? I need them to know you have—"

"Autism. I remember."

A small dialogue box appeared that the teachers had muted their video feed. Belen felt her cheeks warm and wondered when their audio had turned on.

"How long was that on? What did you press, Belen? Get off the computer. What must your teachers think?" Belen's mother looked from Belen to Axel, expecting answers.

Belen felt her anger bubbling into her chest, running acid down her stomach. "How is this my fault? I've been helping you! Axel isn't listening—"

"And you're getting in the way! *A ver,* Axel come here. This thing is for you. The questions are about start. Belen, get out of here." Leslie didn't notice Belen's watering eyes as she focused on trying to unmute herself on Zoom to ask a question.

Belen could scream.

She moved to get her slippers and stepped outside.

The garden was tucked to the side of their backyard, just out of view from their sliding door. The left-hand side of the three by seven structure reining in the plants was clearly Axel's; it was neatly groomed. The popsicle sticks indicated which seasonal spices and herbs were growing. He had refused to plant the sunflower seeds out of season and instead used the seeds Ms. Sherry had gifted him. The plants were coming in nicely, and despite their small stature they were growing in large clumps. On the right-hand side, Belen's struggling plants laid, dead and dying. She had transferred a few plants from their spot on the windowsill to her section. And despite the heatwaves and watering, no amount of care seemed to revive the variety of succulents, aloe vera, and bamboo plants. Her only hope was the sunflowers would bloom to bring some light to her plant cemetery. She moved to check the plants' roots that looked soaked in water. And still, their leaves were curled and brown.

A tear fell from her cheek before she realized she was crying. She tried to muffle her choked gasps for air, but she felt too resentful. She didn't know what else to do.

Nothing seemed to turn out right for her. She had just started her courses and was already falling behind, despite all the study hall, Zoom sessions. Her search for an internship met rejection after rejection. The only source of income required her to wake up at 5 a.m. to tutor LSE students in

Spanish. And she was still contemplating applying to LSE. She just had to press send. And yet, she couldn't make herself do it.

Her anger manifested into her hands as she picked up handfuls of soil. She started to punch the dirt beside her failing plants. She couldn't catch her breath as she continued to pound the earth until she finally released a heaving scream. A high pitched noise reverberated out of her body, lacking bass but filled with pain. She covered her face with her dirt-covered hands.

"Honey, tears make soured herbs."

Belen looked up and saw Ms. Sherry peering over the fence. Her moon-shaped face looked calm, understanding even.

"I'm sorry. I was just—"

"Another woman crying in silence. It seems regardless of the culture, we teach our women to drink our anger and cry in silence."

Belen nodded and tried to wipe off her tears. She stopped when she remembered how dirty her hands were.

"Honey, it's okay. I didn't come here to interrupt."

"No, I'm sorry. I'm just overreacting."

"No, you're *just* reacting. And that's okay."

Belen nodded again and let her tears fall onto her dark jeans. She stayed there, crying quietly, her shoulders shuddering, and Ms. Sherry humming for what felt like an eternity. But the sun soon started to bring the familiar purple lines to the sky, and she remembered her family would soon ask for her, likely as if nothing had happened.

Belen began to stand up and gave Ms. Sherry a watery smile.

Before she turned to leave, Ms. Sherry spoke. "Your plants are being overwatered, over saturated in light, over managed. It's natural for inexperienced gardeners to do too much, too soon. Caring for plants is a tender balance. You provide the basics: sun, air, water, dirt. But the gardener needs to trust the plant can carry on the rest. You can't try to be the plant. You can check in on it, but ultimately you'll have to step away and let it do what it wants."

Belen looked at the mess she had made and wondered how soon Axel would berate her for herbicide.

"Your little plant is managing well. You love him—that's obvious to everyone. You love all of them. But too much can suffocate them. Give them, and yourself, room to breathe. So much has happened so soon. It's okay to have the gardener get some air, step into the sun, stand under some water, and have something to ground them too."

OLIVIA, SCOTTSDALE— OCTOBER 2020

———

Priscila knew.

Olivia had been vigilantly backtracking her own symptoms. She had a cough for a few days before Priscila was getting headaches and eventually a fever. And yet, Olivia never complained, never bothered to take a test.

She had been waiting for Olivia to fess up.

Priscila knew.

They largely stayed away from each other again, but eventually Priscila stopped coming out of her room all together.

Olivia thought it was Priscila's form of punishment. After all, Priscila had the master bedroom with a balcony and private bathroom. Priscila could easily slip in and out of the fire escape and use her mini fridge. Olivia would have done it.

But after a few days, Olivia was getting worried.

Olivia had done her research, and it sounded like she had faced the worst of it. Other than a dry cough and a rash that was taking its sweet time to go away, she felt okay.

But Priscila was nowhere to be seen. Olivia heard muffles from Priscila's room—presumably having calls—and doors closing quietly two nights ago, but usually it was just silence. Olivia figured Priscila's father and brother were remotely checking in on her and she would be fine. Olivia was concerned, but she tried to focus on her followers who were wishing her a quick recovery and sending their thoughts to Priscila.

Still, she lingered near Priscila's door every time she passed the kitchen, hoping to catch some kind of indication Priscila was okay.

***

Turns out, things get better before they get worse.

Olivia stared at Priscila's door from her seat on the couch, as she had been for the last few hours. The TV was muted but alive with color as media covered the latest updates on the president's condition since contracting COVID. Olivia occasionally glanced at the television but kept her focus on the door. She had a letter from the landlord, addressed to Priscila and sublessee, asking to have rent delivered in the next five days to avoid a penalty fee.

Priscila was many things, but she didn't fall behind on rent. And Olivia had actually sent the money to Priscila on time this month; it just didn't make sense.

Olivia hoped Priscila would eventually come out. She was nervous of knocking, unsure if Priscila would reject her concern. Olivia had recovered fairly gracefully and spent the majority of the last week at Steven's since he was granted time off due to his mild COVID symptoms. But she figured the refrigerator would at least show signs of Priscila.

A colony of white mold had taken over the browned apple that laid on top of an orphaned container of Thai food, which also continued to sweat in its container.

Olivia felt her cheeks pulse. She huffed air in and out three times before bringing herself to knock on Priscila's door.

Silence.

A few more raps against the door, harder this time.

Silence.

Olivia pounded against the door, unable to find her voice.

Silence.

Twisting the knob to test the lock, Olivia opened the door and walked in. She tried to make sense of the scene in front of her. She dropped the letter in her hand.

No, things weren't alright. They were much worse than she could have imagined.

***

Olivia's tearful live stream goes viral.

She'd never seen such a huge jump in followers, and though it came with some trolls and critics, the comment section mostly helped her keep it together. The coverage must have been viral for her parents to hear about it.

"How are you doing, sweetheart? Your father is here with me." Her mother sounded concerned enough to warn her of the audience.

Olivia was still reeling from the emotions she had dealt with in the last few days, having to take her last few personal days to recover.

"I'm pushing through it."

"How very brave of you, Olivia." Her father's words were never minced; to hear his sad attempt of counsel was surprising yet... unsettling.

"Thank you, Richard. I'm—" Olivia took a deep breath. "I'm going to be alright. I've been taking advantage of this time to work on what I actually want to do with my platform. And how I can use my voice to show others they are not alone."

"That's so brave. We're so glad to hear you are focusing your energy on something positive. Truly. Aren't we, Richard? We think it's great after seeing your roommate die—"

"She's not dead yet. Her brother said she was just losing consciousness."

Her mother's voice turned sugary sweet when she turned her attention back to Olivia. "Right. Well, that. I'm glad you're taking this with stride. And you are trying to support her. It's so nice of you to speak to young people who are grieving as well."

"Yeah. I mean, no one expects to actually lose someone from this. They resonate with me because I showed them what it was like to grieve and have to figure things out without them. We need to prioritize the mental health of young people. We have to do it for Priscila."

"Poor Priscila. She worked herself ragged. You told me she had been isolating herself lately because she was supporting patients with medical information over the phone. Shocking her parents didn't stop her from pouring herself into the clinic. I mean, you said they were very well off. I'm curious why they didn't use their money to pay for ventilators and all those other things you said the clinic needed, instead of Priscila drafting a last minute will that gifts her entire life savings to funding the clinic. Admirable, but it feels ridicu—"

Olivia's father's voice boomed through the phone. "Rebecca, can you please watch your language? The girl is dead. Her—"

"She's not dead! And Priscila did this herself. I never saw her parents pushing her into this. Vincent said—"

"Is Vincent her boyfriend?"

"Uh, no. It's her older brother. He's in his last year of med school at the University of Wash—"

"Smart young man."

"Are you dating him? Is he cute?"

Her parents seemed to have a one-track mind, as if they were... "Are you both watching the news?"

"We are seeing the developments with the president. See, Richard. The cocktail of drugs seems to be working. Has your roommate's family tried that?"

"Oh, Vincent said they couldn't do all of that because she was picked up a bit too late, since she didn't warn them until her oxygen levels were too low."

Sort of. Apparently, Priscila had been looking into using her savings and retirement funds to help the clinic. She played a risky game by letting the terminal disability kick in, qualifying her to pull out her entire 401K and IRA savings. She was able to get it all transferred before her family could stop her, but she ran out of time to go to the hospital. The idiot.

In some ways, she felt like Priscila was purposely doing this to prove her point. She wished Priscila wasn't such a sacrificial lamb and had just called her brother sooner. Instead, it was 2 a.m. when Vincent picked up his unconscious sister and took her to the hospital, leaving no indication of Priscila's disappearance. And forgetting to contact his sister's roommate to tell her they were going to take her to the hospital for two weeks.

"Hmm, and she's stable?" Her father clearly was multi-tasking.

"Umm, yes. I already told you. She's doing better than they had expected. Not great, but better."

It was a miracle Priscila had stabilized as she had. She had respiratory issues since she was a child, and they were trying to maximize her oxygen levels by laying her on her stomach and putting her on a ventilator.

Still... it had been four days since she had been conscious. Or rather, that was last time Olivia heard from Vincent. He stopped responding to her Facebook messages. She could only guess it was because he was busy caring for his family.

"Sweetheart..."

Olivia knew where this was going and why her parents were talking to her in that tone.

"I... can't."

"You can't be alone in that empty apartment with your roommate's ghost—"

"She's not dead! My god! She can't be dead. Stop saying that. Just please..."

"Okay, okay. I'm sorry. You had mentioned she was fat, so I didn't expect her to do well. But considering the president has bounced back—"

"And he has access to the best medical team. Priscila's family is well off, but they don't have those kind of connections. Not with how she's doing. And she's not fat. I was..." Olivia's throat knotted at the thought of Priscila. "I was just insecure, and she was gaining some weight, so I just... I'm not going back. I can't just leave."

"Why not?" Her father's stern tone felt like a finality.

"Because I can't face everyone. And I can't leave Priscila's stuff here alone."

Her father was quiet for a second, expecting Olivia to throw more excuses. Hearing nothing, he formulaically explained what his daughter refused to accept:

"You wanted to be known. You are. You wanted to escape the rumors that surrounded you here. It's been forgotten. You wanted purpose. You have it. Stay through Thanksgiving if you need to. But it sounds to me like you have outgrown Arizona. And there's nothing wrong with that."

BELEN, LOS ANGELES— OCTOBER 2020

———

Axel's laugh reverberated through the small home.

He was watching skits of the vice presidential debate with a particular focus on a fly. Even Belen's mother had to smile at every eye roll; she occasionally glanced at the television but was mostly glued to her phone. She was on the level 539 of Candy Crush and couldn't seem to pass it.

And in the furthest corner of the house, inside of a small closet lined with shoes, Belen sat. Listening. Breathing. Crying.

She hadn't told her mother, Maggie, or Patrick yet. It was just… she didn't want to do it and be held to it.

And the first session was brutal.

Despite having an hour meeting, they had gone way past that, and time was never mentioned. The therapist— Aly—said Belen was her last client of the day and, as a new client, she felt it was important for Belen to share as much as she wanted.

"I guess, I'm just afraid of—" Belen paused and kept an ear out for any steps approaching her room. "I'm just afraid of what my mom would think. She's gone through so much. She raised strong children, and she needs help, not someone who's falling apart."

Aly had lowered her voice to match Belen's volume. "What makes you say that? Do you think no one would help her?"

"Who would? The system has never been in favor of her. Of us."

"Who is 'the system?'"

"Special victims counsel. The lack of resources that took care of my family after the accident. The school administrators who ignore us when they hear any kind of special requests Axel might need. The teachers who can get away with dismissing him. My mom has gone through so much. She's working long hours, often in jobs she's overqualified for. She *would* get an education, but she's busy being a single mother to two kids, one of which is autistic. She lost her life partner because of the car accident. She lost the last person who would defend her when she was taken advantage of in the military, when she was assaulted, when she was trying to get a degree. My father is gone and no one knocked on her door to see if she was okay."

"What about family? Or the VA?"

Belen sighed. She paused, and peeked her head out of the door. Feeling confident everyone was distracted, Belen closed the door.

"Veteran Affairs... kind of helps. I'm glad we get VA benefits and they've helped my mom with the mortgage payments, because there's no way she could afford this place otherwise. But it's complicated... she was discharged under honorable conditions. And my mother's family is in Honduras and they drifted apart after she joined the army. I'm not sure why, but if I'm speculating... "

"Do you think it was related to distance, or...?"

Leslie was always on her own. She didn't know a life different from caring forward alone.

"Maybe, but it could be the assault making her feel isolated. She had at least the support of her family until she went into the military. From then on, she's been by herself, caring for everyone except herself. I don't know how she does it. I can't imagine what this would feel like without anyone helping me..."

"You're also doing so much for your family, you shouldn't feel guilty for wanting to take a break. And I won't berate you for doing too much—you decide how much is too much. But I would ask you to consider this for the next few weeks, because this process won't fix itself overnight. Ask yourself, do they need you to take care of them, or do they need someone to stand by them as they figure it out?"

Belen listened to Aly, slowly tuning into her surroundings. She nodded but realized Aly wouldn't be able to see it. Belen got up and opened the door.

"I will."

"Okay. Will this time work next week—Sunday, the twenty-fifth, at six at night? We can always reschedule, but having it in our calendars will help establish a routine."

"Yes, that works. Thank you so much, Aly." Belen's voice started to crack, and she willed herself to swallow her tears.

"That's what I'm here for. And... I try to not involve politics or faith, but since you mentioned you were spiritual and politically inclined, please take care—especially with this next debate. Look for ways to center yourself and measure how you're feeling every day. Maybe write it down if you're comfortable. But just check in. Don't judge yourself; just perform a soft body-scan."

"Okay, I will. Thank you again."

"Take care, Belen. Bye."

"Bye." Belen exhaled and rested her hand on her chest. She took a deep breath and held it. Then intentionally pushed it out. She slowly brought her breath in, filling her stomach and her chest. She held it. And slowly released it again.

She stretched her neck and moved to clean her room—the random slippers tossed near her desk, the odd book on her bed, and the chair full of clothes she meant to get to earlier in the week.

But she continued to mindfully inhale and exhale.

***

She didn't understand it.

He would just walk in and just wordlessly stare at her.

So she would stare back.

Sometimes he would lay down on her bed as she studied. Other times, he would sit at her desk and watch a few videos while she laid on the bed.

Sometimes they'd have a conversation—usually about food or something random.

Other times, he'd stay quiet and eventually leave.

It wasn't every day, but it did feel like a routine of his. Every third day, he would come into her room.

"Belen, why do they call it, 'Se le subió el muerto?'"[46]

---

46   Translation: "The dead climbed on top of you"; common phrase to refer to sleep paralysis.

Belen had been typing away and revising her LSE application. She didn't understand why she couldn't hit submit. "Hm, because sleep paralysis is scary. And death is scary." Belen counted the days between her next exams and nearly missed Axel's next comment. "No, that's not why." "Then, why did you ask?" She started to organize her study schedule, trying to fit readings in between her lessons with the European students and her essay writing sessions. Axel still laid on her bed, hands over his chest, with his eyes closed. Belen stopped typing and sighed. "Are you going to tell me why?"

Axel pressed his lips together before he answered:

"When people use the phrase 'the dead have risen on top of you,' it's usually characterizing a sensation of immobility complemented with a difficulty in breathing and pressure on the chest, likely caused by anxiety and panic. And while your brain registers the activity and is conscious, the body lacks muscle tension, the heartbeat and breathing decreases... and for that person, it feels like someone is on top of them... crushing them with their weight... and they're unable to move from their bed... completely powerless to fight for their own survival. Like this virus. We're powerless against it."

Belen slowly turned around, feeling a chill creep up her spine. "We're not powerless, Axel. We have masks, and are social distancing, and—"

Axel looked like a statue. "Those precautions won't stop it from infecting everyone. Not all of us will die. But people like us—like mom—who are exposing themselves every day, making everything move like clockwork, like nothing is wrong, will die. In fact, we die a bit every day."

Belen faced the motionless Axel for a long while. When he twitched, she jumped.

Sweat began to collect on her forehead. It had been months since her last First Aid class, and she wasn't sure she remembered everything she had to do. She looked around for the booklet that laid on her corner nightstand: *First Aid—Seizures (for Parents).*

Axel laid still again.

She let out a practiced breath, willing her heart to slow. She rubbed her trembling hands on her joggers. "Axel?"

"Have you had it?"

"A seizure? No."

"No. The dead. On top of you."

"No, I haven't... Have you?" Belen rarely felt creeped out by things, but the talk of death made her nervous. But she wasn't scared by her own death. Not in the least.

"I have. But usually, I just stare at the ceiling. The dead and I have become friends, so I've stopped trying to move. I've mostly gotten used to it. But... there's someone that keeps appearing. He used to scare me because he was always at the corner of my bed, just out of sight. He had short, black, curly hair. It hurt my vision trying to see that bottom right corner, where he was always just out of sight."

Belen gripped her chair, feeling the hair on her arms rise. She wanted to tell him she wasn't strong enough to talk about this right now... But who else could he go to?

"Each time, I saw a bit more of him. He has brown skin like me. Well, deeper. And his hair was matted, with something... Like a gel, I think. It was goopy and dark. And he had thick eyebrows, the way you draw them in when you want to 'look nice,' and he had a fat nose. A big nose. And big lips too. But I can't see his eyes. They're always closed. But he was crying—his face looked wet. He looked like a vampire, with a trickle of blood coming out of his mouth. But when he tried to speak, his teeth were bloody."

Belen moved to the bed and tried to gently touch Axel's arm trying not to startle him. But he stayed perfectly still, even at her touch.

"I was used to it because I thought it was a vampire in my room, but that's not possible. So I thought it was just a dream." Axel opened his eyes but only stared at the ceiling. "But last night... he tried to grab my foot. And when he turned to grab me, I got a better look at him. He has the same two moles I have near my ear. The more I stared to recognize him, the closer he got. He grabbed my foot, and I woke up. I must have. Because he was gone."

Belen stared at him and didn't want to let go of him. She had a question she couldn't bring herself to ask; an answer she didn't want to hear. But Axel answered it anyway.

"I think it's Dad."

"Axel, how could you know it's him?" Axel looked at his petrified sister, and Belen continued. "Maybe you saw a picture and imagined him."

He shook his head. "This is why I only talk to mom. She likes my ghost stories."

"Stories? How many dead people visit you?" Belen made a mental note to bless the house with the holy water they bought from the Placita Olvera the moment she finished reviewing her application.

"We're all almost dead, Belen. Don't be so afraid of death. Jennifer says—"

"Who is Jennifer?"

"My academic counselor. She lets me call her Jennifer. Anyway, Jennifer says when people's bodies stop working, they die. But as we grow older, eventually, small pieces of us stop working until our bodies stop working altogether. That's why Ms. Cynthia isn't going to meet with me anymore. She's like Dad. She's dead."

Belen's eyes widened. "When did she pass?"

"Pass what?" Axel sat up, confused.

"I meant, when did she die?"

"Oh, two weeks ago."

"Are you okay, Axel?"

"I'm okay—I'm still alive."

"Axel…" Belen stared at her brother. In some ways, he was the smartest person in the room. In others, Belen still saw the small boy who would cry over his toy trains when they were out of order.

Belen tried to practice intentional breathing, even if she looked crazy. She needed to reassure him. "If you need me, I'm right here."

"I know. That's why I'm here." Belen held him to her, feeling him trying to pull away but ignoring it. She knew he was annoyed with her, but she didn't care. She squeezed him harder. As she stared at a picture of her mother and brother at her high school graduation on her nightstand, she pushed herself to talk.

"Hey, can I ask you something?"

"You already have."

"Okay… well, how would you feel if I went to London to study after I graduated?"

Axel stopped struggling to get out of her hug. "Wouldn't it feel the same way it does when you went to study abroad? What's the difference?"

She pulled away and looked at him, feeling her eyes water.

"I don't know. I guess not much."

LEILANI, EMERYVILLE— OCTOBER 2020

———

She had been avoiding the conversation entirely. He wouldn't let it go.

Even as she carried her groceries into her apartment, she couldn't get it out of her head. How was she supposed to introduce him to her father? She didn't know how her father would react, but she couldn't think of a scenario where her father welcomed him with open arms.

It had been three weeks since the call, but Joanna and Mrs. Boutros were constantly asking about her, according to Michael. Especially Joanna.

His little sister was excited at the idea of working at a law firm, especially since she thought it would give her an edge on her college applications.

And it was cute. It was heartwarming for Michael's family to be so willing to check in on her. But that meant Michael was constantly reminded he hadn't been introduced to her own family.

Her mental debate was so distracting she almost missed the sirens.

Though COVID cases had gone down in San Francisco, Leilani had grown accustomed to hearing ambulances flying through the streets to overheated elders in nearby nursing homes. But this time, the sirens grew louder. As she got off the elevator and entered her apartment, she didn't even bother sanitizing her doorknob and instead ran to look at what was happening outside through her balcony.

And so had most of the residents in her complex. On either side, her neighbors peered down to see the procession. Someone was being taken out of the building, the body covered in a white sheet.

"My god." Leilani turned to her right and saw a young Black guy looking at his phone. She had turned away, but she couldn't help but notice how well dressed he was, despite it being a typical Tuesday evening. His chestnut loafers, form fitting khakis, crisp white crew neck shirt, and aviator sunglasses looked so intentional.

He must have sensed her gaze because he looked up, suddenly, his tight curls lightly bouncing up before gently aligning themselves along his chiseled jawline.

"Hi there."

Leilani felt too aware of her gray yoga pants and white oversized t-shirt, her hair gathered in a curled poof. "Uh, hi. Do you know what's going on downstairs?"

He glanced over the railing, letting his sunglasses slightly slip down his nose. He turned to look at her again before checking his phone. "Yeah, Ms. Adamson passed away. It was announced in the building group app."

Leilani jerked her head. She ignored the building's bulletin board on the rare days she left her apartment, but she didn't think she was so out of the loop she missed the building's app.

The stranger glanced at her before scrolling on his phone again. "Are you new here? I thought I recognized you, but everyone in this building is on it, unless... you must be the infamous Manfred."

Manfred? Leilani continued to stare at him and had half a mind to ask him, but the sirens signaled they were getting ready to depart. "Where did Ms. Adamson live?"

"Hm? Oh, she was on the floor below us, and should be about..." He turned around and oriented himself. "She would be about three doors left of the elevator." He quirked an eyebrow and pursed his lips to the left.

"Were you close to her?" Leilani leaned on the railing, looked on either side of her balcony, suddenly wishing she had decorated more of it.

He took a step backward as if to leave, but he paused. "Wow, you must really be as recluse as everyone says. Yeah, she was a super sweet lady. Quite the character. Very independent, but she always had a story to share if you were willing to listen. Or even if you didn't. She—why don't you join the memorial service? I could try to give you a rendition of one of her stories, but I'd never be able to do it justice."

"Sure. Is there a link, or—"

"I'll airdrop you my contact and send you the link. What's your name again?"

"Leilani. Alexander."

"Very regal. I'm Christian Walker. I moved in a few months ago, from Castro."

"Nice. Well, welcome. I hope Emeryville is exciting enough after living in the city."

"Oh, I've outgrown excitement, sweetheart. I'm actually looking for a change in pace." He raised his hand and gave her a smile before going back into his apartment.

***

"Thank you so much for joining us!" A peppy blonde took over as host of the Zoom memorial call. Her enthusiasm would be appreciated anywhere else but here. Still, she continued to speak in her high-pitched voice.

"Now, though her children, Benji and Annalise, have decided to mourn in private, as residents of the building, we wanted to provide a forum to mourn the loss of one of our own, Ms. Lauren Adamson." The blonde began to share her screen and started a slideshow that showcased a young woman's image. It was clear the image was old; the young woman had a Sears-type headshot, with faux fur falling off of her shoulders and a pearl necklace around her throat. Her warm, fawn skin glowed, and her beautiful, curled tresses were pulled back to reveal her face. Leilani couldn't help but return a smile at the young Lauren's "Colgate smile."

When the slideshow shifted to announce the next speaker in the memorial, Leilani decided to grab her chicken Alfredo pasta from the fridge. Even as the new speaker initiated a prayer and made initial introductions, Leilani focused on fixing her dinner.

"Ms. Lauren was an incredible storyteller. She was never shy to share information about her past, as a volunteer firefighter, runaway teenager, or when she fell on hard times and worked as a coat check at a burlesque show. When her husband passed while her kids were young, Mrs. Adamson continued to work multiple jobs and never let her dream die. She continued to provide for her family and began to design clothes, her ultimate dream. Though none of us were graced with wearing her designs, she modeled them every day and paired them with colorful hats and canes to match each of her creations." Leilani jolted and ran to the screen. "Queen E" and her bright highlighter yellow hats with a black cane and sparkling black dress appeared in the next sequence, confirming Leilani's denial. The woman Michael and she teased had died... Something within Leilani broke, knowing she would never show up again in her full getup.

"She was a joy to be around because she could take any tragedy into a laughable moment. We'd like to think even with the tragic circumstances that lead to her death, she could find something to sass at. She laid alone for three days, unable to lift herself up after injuring her back. In such a situation, she might say, 'Where's the landlord when you need him? It's the first of the month, and he would have been here knocking!'" The new speaker, a brunette with prominent eyebrows and big blue doe eyes, paused for a moment, trying to release the last few words without choking on them in a watery laugh.

"She was the kind of woman who wouldn't take hell from anyone. And though she wasn't able to reconcile with her estranged children after she came out, I'd like to think she knew she was loved by us. It hurts us to know she was isolated for loving who she loved. We love you Ms. Lauren. Rest in Peace." The brunette immediately switched off her video feed, leaving a shocked Leilani searching for a cue from other attendees on how to react. Instead, they stopped sharing screens and switched to the next speaker: Christian.

Christian sighed and looked straight at the camera. "I had recently moved in when Ms. Lauren walked past me in her incredible, bubble gum pink suit. You can't watch a woman in her eighties, with so much swagger, walk by without telling her that her threads are incredible. And in typical Ms. Lauren fashion, she walked back, giving her best runway strut, and told me, 'I know. You can't copy originality.' And she launched into a ninety-minute conversation about the latest designs from New York Fashion Week and the cultural significance of having power houses not appearing this year. This woman was a force to reckon with. The only ones strong enough to face her were her two arch nemesis: tight jars and her upstairs neighbor, who she dubbed 'Manfred' or 'Manny.' That woman and Manny were like water and oil."

All of the tiles on the screen reflected people shaking in seeming laughter. The chat immediately began to populate with laughing emoticons.

"Ms. Lauren was a special soul, but she did not take well to hearing every step and groan of her neighbor. Her upstairs neighbor's leg 'dragged like a log or an impetuous child—there was no in-between!' She would even carry a broom to nudge her neighbor to lower her voice or tread lightly. Every bang of her broom was met with a muffled whine or stomp. I don't know why they never met, but Ms. Lauren had a story ready about Manny. She named her upstairs neighbor after the recluse mammoth in *Ice Age* who only complained and paced every day, and she wondered why their neighbor never seemed to leave their apartment even before COVID happened. Though Manny drove her insane, Ms. Lauren drowned out the noise with her sewing machine. And if she leaves nothing else, we need to carry on Ms. Lauren's legacy—we will work through the hate, the pain, and the annoyance of our life. Because the final product is always worth it. I didn't know her long, but you don't need to in order to appreciate everything she was."

Leilani shut off her computer.

She let the sorrow that threatened to spread and consume her sit alongside her. Had Ms. Adamson been using the broom to contact her when she laid on the ground, alone? Was *she* so isolated no one would realize she was dead until it was too late? Covered in one's own fluids and...

Leilani went into her room, looking at the empty carpeted space between the door and her bed. Wondering and begging to know if Queen E had expressed any bangs for help—and if she had been so distracted they went ignored. She was so spiteful at the banging she never investigated the source of the noise.

Leilani fell to her knees, unable to wash off the sadness that prevailed. She laid on the ground, alone, bothered and guilty.

***

Michael was twelve minutes away.

He had been upset for the past few weeks due to the upcoming election and announced he was going to stay over at hers. Apparently, San Francisco was yet again preparing for war, terrorism, racism, and their own residents. Cartier was boarded up; DWS had a plank graffitied with "We're still open!" A lone bankrupt bar left a sign that evidently represented everyone living below the poverty line: "Broken into already—nothing left." Michael's pictures on his way to brunch with his friends did little to quell their fears on the upcoming election's potential aftermath.

Michael's Uber was seven minutes away, coming off the freeway and waiting at a light.

He had been hanging out with his friends, now that he was getting tired of the virus, and likely getting tired of her. Leilani had been ignoring everyone, even her friends who kept tagging her on memes and videos to entice her in joining them for a chat. She couldn't stand the silence in her apartment but wouldn't let herself be surrounded by noise. Leilani carefully tread around the apartment and bought carpets and rugs to smother her footsteps.

Only for her to pull them off and listen for signs of life from the apartment below.

Leilani had largely ignored her sisters' messages about logistics for Thanksgiving. She couldn't help but watch herself drown. She deleted her social media apps and would have blocked Michael if he didn't threaten to reach out to her sisters. Even still, with his pending arrival, she held her tea, laid on the couch, ABC on silent and captioned, and a weighted blanket holding her in place.

A message from Michael alerted her he had arrived... she would need get up and face him.

Leilani stared at George Stephanopoulos, watching him garble more hypotheticals—nearly nonsensically, considering the circumstances. What was the point of guessing the next president? Or even next year? Nothing had changed.

A knock at the door forced Leilani to grip her mug harder. But she willed her body up and proceeded to make her way to answer it, one step at a time. Her legs felt heavier as they dragged along the floor, quietly covering ground.

Another knock, more urgent now, made her heart race. But her legs were still struggling to reach the destination. She would use her voice, if she hadn't lost it too.

When the door handle was within reach, the weight of her legs seemingly doubled, unwillingly to compromise another inch. She sighed and chewed on her tongue.

She opened the door to reveal an anxious Michael dialing her phone.

"Where's your phone?"

Leilani pointed at the couch. Michael stomped inside, blundering into the room. He put his things in her bedroom and returned to the living room, finding Leilani wrapped in her blanket. Though Leilani had always carried a tinier frame, her height gave her a presence that was hard to ignore.

And yet she nearly disappeared into the white cotton blanket, swept into its warmth, hidden under its weight.

"Leilani, what's going on? You've hardly talked to me in the last month. I thought we were okay after talking to my parents."

She started to regret not replying to him. They had agreed they would quarantine between Michael seeing his friends and spending time with her. However, Leilani had taken the opportunity to ghost all of the messages he sent her in the last three weeks.

"Hello? Leilani? You've been pulling away. Is it bothering you? Is it angering you I'm spending time with them? Or I'm meeting up with them? Is it your family? Do you feel okay?"

Leilani could have scoffed. She welcomed the time away from everyone. There was something soothing about wallowing in her own misery that gave her the time to not be happy. To not be okay.

Michael moved to sit near Leilani, but was unsure if the six feet apart would still apply considering the circumstances. Leilani vacantly looked at him, unmoving.

"You need to talk to me. I can't have you stonewalling me. I can't do this with you."

Leilani stared at him, his beard quickly growing around face and threatening to consume it. He looked tired.

"I'm okay with you seeing them."

"Okay. Then what is it? I know you've been ignoring me. You hardly react to my messages. You say you're too busy to video chat. I ask you questions and you're flippant. Talk to me—I can help if you talk to me."

His hazel eyes looked browner now, matching his jerry curls. Leilani hadn't noticed before how his eyes became more animated with the right amount of adrenaline.

"I'm just tired."

"Leilani, you need to talk to me. C'mon. I need you to tell me what's wrong." Michael moved closer but stopped his hands from cradling her chin.

"I don't know what you want me to say."

"You have been acting weird for weeks now! Are you trying to push me away? Do you want this to end? I'm not the only one in this relationship, love."

"No... I don't want this to end." Leilani sighed, but she couldn't stare into his eyes.

"Then what's wrong? What did I do—did I say something? Am I rushing you? Overwhelming you?" Michael gripped the couch as he knelt in front of Leilani.

Leilani stared at him and felt her eyes water. She knew this was inevitable, but she thought she had more time.

Michael cradled her hand, his face blotchy and red. "How can I fix it?"

Leilani sighed. "I'm not okay right now. I just..." She looked up when she heard two thumps from upstairs. And her cry could not escape her dry mouth.

"Are you done with me, Leilani?" Michael's face looked blank, but his watery, bloodshot eyes told a different story.

"I don't know what I need. But it's not fair for me to have you here when I don't know, and you clearly do."

Michael's tears framed his face. He kissed her hand, tenderly, and let a tear roll off onto it before he got up. Standing, he croaked one last sentence:

"Were you ever even planning on introducing me to your family?"

BELEN, LOS ANGELES— NOVEMBER 2020

———

She was finalizing the last touches on the Christmas tree. She had shifted some of the decorative balls to the sparser areas and was adjusting the garland. She knew it was a bad idea to decorate in her Thanksgiving clothes, but her mother and brother had kicked her out of the kitchen. They said they were going to treat her to her holiday favorites since she had just finished several exams and decided she deserved a break. She was all too happy to let them do it, seeing as Axel was excited to do something that wasn't inappropriate, like cuss out his teacher or have a total meltdown while doing his homework.

She had offered to clean and set the table, but after they pushed her out, she instead got ready to parade her nicest outfit around the living room. She had decided to wear her hair natural, letting the soft curls hang around her face as the turtleneck sweaterdress clung to her athletic frame. Though she had no one to impress, she had used all of her newly-found free time to experiment with her eye makeup, adding glitters she had long left untouched since before the pandemic.

When her mother came in to ask her to start setting up the Christmas tree as per Thanksgiving tradition, she complimented her daughter and hugged her. Even though her daughter was an even six inches taller, Leslie was so happy to see her dolled up and gave her one extra squeeze.

Walking into the dining room, Belen smelled her favorite food: Honduran pork leg sandwiches. She felt her stomach grumble in anticipation, and it garnered laughter from her mother and brother. As her mother brought up stories about their family, her brother, in careful measure, moved the nuégados de yuca[47] slowly into the deep pot of hot melted piloncillo with anise stars, cloves, black peppers, and cinnamon. Belen moved through the kitchen to serve large cups of Coca-Cola—and she added a bit of Flor de Caña rum to her mother's and her own soft drink. Turning up the music on their television, Belen began to dance with her mother. Her mother tried to get Axel on his feet, but he was too preoccupied with the yucca fritters he ignored their implications.

Belen started to feel the drinks hit her, and she realized she still hadn't had anything to eat since that morning's baleadas.[48] Trying to slow down, she started to sip on water and steal pieces of meat whenever her brother wasn't looking.

A few hours later, their mother ushered them to set the table. As Belen neatly decorated the table with festive gold

---

47 Translation: [Honduran dish] cassava fritters
48 Translation: A traditional Honduran dish composed of a flour tortilla, filled with mashed fried red beans (a variety of beans native from Central and South America), thick Honduran cream (mantequilla), and crumbled hard salty cheese.

and red table mats and decorative plates, she paused at the fourth chair. She decided to set a fourth placemat and adjust the square table so the food would be neatly displayed—the fourth setting would host the tripod. She ran into her bedroom and did one last thing before displaying the food.

When her mother came out of the bedroom, donned in a red dress shirt with jeans and heels, she gasped. She didn't say anything else and hugged Belen. When Axel exited his bedroom a few minutes later, he looked confused seeing a picture frame in the center of the fourth placemat. He approached the seat and inspected the space before gasping at asking. "Is that Dad?"

Belen and Leslie nodded.

Beautifully plated sandwiches with home dressing accompanied flute glasses filled with sparkling cider and bowls of nuégados in its syrup. A piece of the pork leg was showcased in the center, surrounded with the elements to construct a second or third helping. But the forth place setting had a tripod set with an iPad with images of their father playing in a montage. And below him was Axel's toy drum set.

Axel looked at Belen. "Why are my drums in the center of the table?"

"Because we need to be thankful and remember someone very important to us. In our family, we play the drums a year and a day after the person has…" Belen paused to exhale before continuing, "…died to remember to celebrate their life and they've been freed of suffering."

"Hm. So it's a tradition? But it hasn't been a year and a day since dad died—it's been years!"

Their mother stepped in. "But it's Thanksgiving. And today, when we are remembering to be thankful, it makes sense to bring back one tradition even during another celebration."

Axel stayed quiet but contemplated the drums. Belen made sure the stove was off, before her family gathered in prayer and began to eat.

***

After hours of bothering Axel, Belen's mother finally got him to dance with her deep into the night. Belen would take turns with Axel, but no one could match her grad-student-on-break energy levels. As the witching hour approached, Belen felt everyone slow, and they eventually allowed the couch to comfort their tired bodies.

It didn't take long for Axel to start snoring after he fell asleep on his mother's lap. Belen puckered her mouth to point at Axel. Her mother had been enjoying the loud music, but noticed Belen's nudge and decided to lower the volume on their television. They had refused to turn on the news.

A newscaster's voice was replaced with their own, and it was a welcomed change.

"Oh Mami, Ms. Sherry gave us some wine before she left to see her grandchildren."

"We need to make sure we have something nice ready for her. We'll give her food and a new bottle of rum. She's been so good to Axel."

Belen looked at her mother. "What happened to 'stranger danger?' Suddenly you're okay with the neighbor talking to us?" Belen laughed. "Axel has made you more trusting. It's a good thing."

Her mother tsked with approval. "Of course he has. I can't do everything, as much as I want to. And I've seen her for years. We say hello. I know she's respectful without crossing the line. She talks to Axel quite a lot. Y'know? He keeps tending to that garden, and he's actually enjoying it. He's angry all the time, but now it's less intense."

Belen looked down at Axel with his mouth open, breathing through it and occasionally twitching.

"I didn't realize that. I'm glad it's helping him. It's hard to know when things are helpful."

"We don't say it enough, but we are so happy to have you home. It's nice to have my little ducks all back, but I also know you've had it rough. I don't want our home life to distract you from work though. You need to focus on your education. It's the only thing no one, no man, could ever take away from you. It's worth millions."

Belen laid her head back onto the couch. "Really though. It's costing me millions." Belen groaned into her hands, willing herself to not think about her financial woes.

"Belen, it'll be worth it. Don't worry about that."

"Mami, I see how much I'll owe. I'm going to be in debt for the rest of my life. I could never own a home. I'll be fifty and still paying off my student loans. How could I ever take care of you and Axel?"

"Mi amor, that's what my Social Security is for. I didn't fight to get citizenship to have you worry about this. And so what if you owe forever? And? You could be making enough to cover it or apply to that Public Service Loan Forgiveness program they mentioned at Axel's 'Road to College' workshop. There's ways to lessen that burden. It's not perfect, but there are ways. Ay mi niña, te complicas la vida."[49]

Belen felt her vision get blurry. She tried to look elsewhere to hide it or find a good reason to walk away, but her mother must have sensed her tears.

---

49 Translation: Oh my girl, you complicate your (own) life.

"Why are you crying? Are you on your period?"

"No! I'm just…" Belen looked at her with a grateful pout. "You've done so much, and after I graduate it's supposed to be my turn to take care of you guys, and it's so selfish to try to prolong that."

"Prolong what?"

"My education… Mami… I really want to go to LSE. They have an incredible international relations program, and I could graduate within a year if I work hard enough. But applying means…"

"How many times have I told you?" Belen was not used her mother's scolding and she felt like she was a little girl again. Her mother leaned toward her, careful not to wake the slumbering Axel.

"You cannot use us as an excuse to not study. Do it now before you have kids. Before you have a husband. I worked hard to see your dream come true. If this is that, do it. Did you apply?"

"I did."

"Good." Her mother leaned back. "Don't be stupid. I want you to live a wonderful life. If it means you have a bit of debt, so be it. It'll give you a great credit score… So how long have you been holding that in?"

Belen couldn't stop her tears now.

"For a while. I was so scared of leaving you all behind. I knew things were rough, here but seeing the mortgage payments scared me. And Axel was misbehaving and struggling with classes… I just thought it would be better if I stayed here."

"And do what? The same thing my mother did and clean the house? You don't need to go to college to do that. And those are my problems *I'm* fixing—I can do this. But maybe

I have been sharing too much. And I don't need you to worry about things you don't need to think about. I'm figuring it out. We're okay."

Belen's water smile was answered with an extended arm. Belen rested on her mother's breast, listening to her steady heartbeat. After a minute of silence, she felt strong enough to ask the question that had been haunting her for months.

"Mami, why don't you talk to your family anymore? Or Dad's?"

Her mother sighed but her heartbeat stayed steady.

"Because they struggled to stay here. When I came to Miami, this country made it possible for me to join the military and get citizenship through your father, but my sisters and mother ran into issues and had to go back to Honduras. And when I came out of the military, they were all back home and I was married. In some ways, I never understood why they left me behind. There's more to it, but I can't explain it to you right now... It's complicated. As for your father's family, my mother-in-law never really liked me. The entire family blames me for his death since we were arguing when the car accident happened, but..."

"It's complicated?"

"No, it's actually very clear. She's a bitch. But I didn't know how to face her without feeling guilty. So I stayed alone with you both. I would take you to see his family more when you were younger, but it was getting nastier every visit. And they didn't understand Axel, so I stopped visiting."

"Maybe that's why Dad haunts us."

"That does sound like something he'd do. He's still an ass in the afterlife." She chuckles. "But he's my asshole."

"You miss him."

"Of course I do. Every day. And I swear I see him some-times. I used to talk to a therapist when you were little because I was scared. But then, I realized I was more scared he would go away forever if I talked to one. I would rather have him as my little shadow."

Belen snugged her head under Leslie's chin and pressed her ear to her mother's heart. She listened to Leslie's heartbeat for a few seconds before she took a breath and said it. "I'm seeing one. A therapist."

Her mother's fingers combed through Belen's curls, each ringlet bouncing back into its shape. But Leslie didn't say anything.

Belen heavily exhaled once more. "We're talking about things that are stressing me out and how I might be doing too much. I might be a little…" She paused to remember the word Aly used to describe her tendencies. "…co-dependent. And I need to start asking if someone even *wants* my help. Because I could be doing all of this work, tiring myself out, and that person might not want it."

Her mother hummed in agreement.

Belen dug her head further into her mother's chest and blurted out, "I think she might be right. So I'm going to try to keep letting go. Because you guys will be okay without me."

Her mother tsked again. "Oh, I could have told you that for free."

"Mom, it *is* free."

"Clearly. I'm glad you're talking to someone, but it does worry me you didn't feel comfortable talking to me."

Belen shifted and turned her neck to look up at her mother.

"Mami, it has nothing to do with it. It took Maggie's insis-tence, Patrick's pushing, Ms. Sherry's—"

"Who's Patrick? A boyfriend?" Her mother nearly woke up Axel with her sudden movement.

"Mami, no! He's my mentor who is reviewing my application and has a fiancé."

Her mother tsked yet again but didn't say anything else.

"Anyway, they've all pushed me to apply to the program and to see a therapist. And my therapist is helping work through a lot of things, including our resident ghost. But I don't think it's a bad thing."

"The haunting?"

"No, having the ghost leave. He's worried. But if he feels good about leaving us to take care of ourselves, he might be able to finally rest."

"That would make one of us." Axel slowly got up, clearly annoyed at being woken up.

"Brush your teeth and pray." Belen and her mother stared at each other after saying it at the same time. Axel shook his head and kissed them each on the top of their heads.

They prayed over him and let him get ready for bed.

Belen and her mother stayed in the living room, with the music playing at a low volume and Belen's mother caressing her head full of curls.

"I think you could all use some rest."

Belen took that statement as a signal to get ready for bed. But when she got up and turned around to look at her mother, she saw her eyes: bloodshot with dark circles underneath.

"You too, Mami."

They shut off the television, checked the locks, and cleaned up the dining room as best as possible, leaving a bit of work for the morning.

When they bid each other good night and prayed over each other, Belen kissed her mother's forehead. "Will you try to talk to someone? About Dad?"

Her mother looked at her and smiled. She leaned over her and kissed her forehead.

"I'll think about it. Will you go to LSE?"

Belen rolled her eyes. "I have to get in first."

"Will you go to LSE?"

Belen smiled and hugged her mother. She took a breath.

"If I get accepted, I'll find a way to go. I'll *make* a way if necessary."

OLIVIA, SCOTTSDALE— NOVEMBER 2020

She adjusted her black dress once more. Her burgundy lip stain had started to smear, and she opted to put on a gloss to hide the mistakes. She checked her email and made sure she had prepaid for a third piece of luggage.

She knew the rest of her things would come back with the movers, but she preferred to take as much as she could with her. She noticed an email that mentioned her verification form and moved to grab her laptop. With the lack of seating options, she decided to place her laptop on top of the granite island to fill out her I-9 form.

Within minutes, she finished submitting the form and replied to Karen, sharing in the excitement to be joining her as a mental health advocate and face of the organization. As she hit send, her inbox was hit with another reminder: "Please respond: Remembering Priscila Fuentes on December 1."

She tried to delete it and instead opened the message.

"Join us in remembering an incredible young woman, devoted to her community, cherished by her family and friends. We will share information for the memorial that will be hosted on Priscila's birthday, January 21, 2021."

She moved it to spam.

Vincent eventually had replied to her. He apologized for the delay, but his family had been inconsolable and working through to support the growing number of patients. Though Priscila's last wish had ensured the clinic would be on solid footing for the next few months, Priscila hadn't thought through how broken the family would be trying to help others while also trying to mourn.

Olivia couldn't do it.

When she heard Priscila's mother open the door, Olivia hid in her room. She had the door cracked open enough to see Mrs. Fuentes roam the space. Priscila was right. Her mother's presence was louder than her own voice. She said nothing. Even as she selected, caressed, and kissed trinkets, plushies, blankets, sweaters, and clothes from Priscila's room and the common areas, Priscila's mother never outwardly cried.

When Olivia had to unfortunately grab her meal prepped food, Priscila's mother nodded and told her "hello." And gave nothing else. Priscila's mother moved and acted like she was completely alone. It felt like an intrusion to view a mother grieve a child, but Olivia couldn't look away. Every item Priscila's mother touched looked like a goodbye. Even the smallest of things like makeup or a shoe were held with the same level of attention. Like a ghost, her mother circled around the room, collecting select items.

Olivia saw Priscila in her. She never really remembered Priscila was Asian until she mentioned it or bought an interesting ingredient. But her nose, mouth, and chin were her mother's. The hair must have been too, though her mother's looked silkier even in the bun she had it in. There wasn't much other resemblance. But in her movement, in her voice, her silence, there was Priscila.

She wondered if Priscila told her how she got COVID. Or if she even needed to.

Olivia felt an apology coming up her throat, but after seeing Priscila's mother side eye her, she stopped. She knew. Of course she knew.

Olivia grabbed her food and ran into her bedroom. She made sure to wait until the late morning the next day to leave her room. When Vincent came by the following weekend, he had the apartment cleared within hours.

Olivia wasn't there that time.

So she agreed. She agreed to come back. And it seemed New York agreed to have her back. Soon after her decision, a couple of organizations asked her to work as a mental health advocate and use her platform to encourage young people to seek counseling. She found herself perplexed and too happy to question the bout of good news.

So she found herself in the middle of an empty apartment. The large kitchen leading into the living room area looked odd. The doors that faced each other in the meridian attempted to reflect symmetry. Instead, it made the space feel like a small bubble full of tension, ready to pop.

Not being able to tolerate the space any longer, Olivia grabbed her sunglasses, her carry-on, and her luggage, struggling but effectively shutting the door behind her.

LEILANI, HOUSTON— NOVEMBER 2020

Leilani waited for the familiar family truck when a gray Lincoln rolled in front of her.

She had flown to Katy, Texas, after her last conversation with Michael in a desperate effort to put some physical space between them. Even though he had moved back to Chicago, her apartment still had memories of them together. She hadn't responded to her sisters' questions in the group chat and fully expected to have a long line of questioning at her father's home.

Leilani stepped back and made way for someone to claim the Lincoln Navigator. The car window rolled down, and Candice leaned over to yell at her to get in. Though surprised, Leilani complied and sat shotgun.

"Hi, Can—"

"Don't 'Hi, Candy' me. Why are you ignoring us? You email us your flight and expect us to just show up? What the hell, Lani?"

Leilani didn't think she would be bombarded with questions so soon.

"Look… it's been complicated in California, and I just needed some time to think."

"Okay, but can you think and let us know how you're doing? Or do you think we're all having fun? Do you not give a fuck on how Dad is doing? Or how we are all away from each other and dealing with the pandemic? You're alone in California, and we have no way to know how you're doing, how to send you things you need. Did you know I had to message one of your friends to find out where you live? What if you were dying? How the fuck am I supposed to know? You're selfish. You know that, right?"

Leilani snapped her neck to her left. Candice was wearing a black turtleneck and black slacks, clearly ready for any last minute legal appointment. It didn't matter she was on the phone all day and was rarely seen. Her ringlets were styled to frame her face, and her Hermes perfume coated the car with a clean floral scent.

But to Leilani, the smell was offensive.

Even in the presence of family, Candice brought her work home and was just as inaccessible in-person due to her standoffish personality. She was always a caricature of who she felt she had to be.

Of whom they both needed to be.

"I guess we all are. But tell me, Candice, how's that crown they've placed on your head? Is it weighing heavy now that you're back and you have to try to be perfect in front of our family? Now you can't hide?" They were a few streetlights away from their father's home, but this wasn't a discussion that was close to ending anytime soon. It was too late. It was all coming out.

Candice shook her head but didn't look away from the road. "You know, people really are ungrateful."

"They are. And selfish. But someone has to be there to catch the family when they fall. Pay a penance for their mistakes. I am sorry for not responding and stressing you all out, but what good does it do me to lie to you? What good does it do me to pretend I'm following in your footsteps? I'm not going to live in fear of rejection because I'm not something you all were expecting." Leilani sighed and looked out the window. "You did help me, Candice. But don't pretend like I didn't cover for you. I'm not the reason you're able to live freely away from here. Dad threw a fit when you left, and you reminded him he had the rest of us. Now that everyone is grown, I'm the only one still under the microscope. I am the one who's analyzed—not you."

"Oh god, Leilani. You act like no one else is living through this. We all have pressure from Dad to be something. I just thought you were grateful enough to appreciate we did everything for you. The least you could've done was keep us updated. I swear, the younger generation grows up to be sensitive about everything." Candice never bothered to glance at Leilani as they approached the third to last streetlight before reaching their old neighborhood.

Leilani stared at her, her face contoured in disgust.

"This isn't about being grateful! Candice, you want to know why I don't tell you guys anything? Really? It's not because I don't care about you guys. Actually, I do a lot, which is why I never told you I had an abortion!"

Candice slammed on the brakes and was nearly rear-ended by the car behind her. She looked at Leilani for a moment before the driver of the car behind her laid on the horn. She reluctantly put the car back into drive and pulled into the nearest fast-food restaurant parking lot. She continued to not say anything, even when she turned off the ignition. She eventually turned to Leilani.

"Why... When?"

"Earlier this year... I found out when Dad had gotten sick. That's why I flew back to California so soon. I just finished paying it off." Leilani stared at her palms, wondering if they would feel itchy again and what it would mean for her in the future.

"Did he—who was...?"

"My boyfriend. Well, ex-boyfriend. We just broke up. He knew."

Candice instinctively snapped. "He told you to get rid of it?"

"No. If anything, he probably wished I kept it. He's Catholic, but he supported my decision. If anything, I think it broke him to know it happened, but he never said as much."

"Did he go to a Jesuit school? A Catholic Black boy—"

"Uh, actually, he wasn't Black." Leilani shook her head as she looked up and faced Candice. "He was Middle Eastern. Is, I mean. He's Lebanese."

Candice dropped into her seat, crossing her arms, an odd expression on her face.

"So you had a White boyfriend running around while you were home in March?"

Leilani crossed her arms and leaned into her seat. "He's Middle Eastern, but yeah... "

Candice began to laugh. Leilani dug herself into her seat. When Candice gained control of her laughter, she noted Leilani's defensive stance.

"Oh, calm down. I'm not making fun of you. It's just... we had a bet going with Makellah and Aisha if you were a lesbian. Honestly, I was in on it. But this makes more sense. Makellah is going to have a ball. She bet good money it was a boy."

"You guys bet on my love life?"

Candice raised an eyebrow. "You'd be bored too if you had to stay with Dad through May; you already know he still treats us like teenagers. Of course we made a bet."

Candice looked ahead but glanced at Leilani from the corner of her eye. "But I get why you hid it from Dad. It would probably kill him if he knew you were dating a White passing guy after he came back from the hospital and everything that went down with Mom… I get it. I just don't get why you didn't tell us. I think even Zoë would have kept her mouth shut."

Leilani looked down at her hands again and shrugged. "None of us were okay when Mom left. And I didn't want y'all to think I was leaving you behind for a 'White guy' too. But it doesn't matter now. It's over."

"Why is it over? It's a pandemic—it's not like he could have cheated on you." Candice gasped. "Oh no—or did he?"

"No, he did absolutely nothing wrong."

"Okay, let me clarify this much. We all do *something* wrong—just because he didn't pick a fight, it doesn't mean something wasn't wrong, or you'd still be with him."

Leilani bit her lip. She stopped writing to Michael after she met his parents and hadn't been able to explain this feeling. So how could she verbalize it now?

Candice placed her hand on hers; Leilani couldn't help but cry yet again.

"My elderly neighbor passed away not too long ago… She was living alone because her family had abandoned her. I joined her memorial and I found out she died in her home without any help for three days. The smell probably made someone check on her. She hadn't made amends with her kids, and... I don't want to die that way, Candy. It's why I hadn't seen Michael for a while. And I do love him, but..."

"You stupid girl." Candice pulled Leilani into an embrace and let Leilani cry on her shoulder. "You stupid, stupid girl. We would never turn our backs on you because you decided to sleep with a White man. Hell, I bet Zoë has dated outside of our race and hasn't told us either." Candice looked down to give her younger sister a small smile. "And Dad... look, I can't promise to change him, but he loves you too much to lose you. And you have to trust us on that. I get those fears—I really do. But no relationship is easy."

"I know." Leilani couldn't prevent the hiccups that ensued. "But after meeting his family, I saw the look his dad gave me. Michael thinks it's in my head or the fact I'm not super religious or I'm just not Catholic. But Candy, I know his dad saw me next to his son and decided he would never accept me. And fuck, I love that man. But I don't want him to be separated from his family because of me. I don't want to be the wedge."

Candice continued to smooth out Leilani's curls and twisted her hair ends. "I know, sweetheart. I know. I respect that. Just... mhm."

Leilani, still hiccupping, raised her eyes. "What?"

Candice bumped their foreheads together, allowing their spirals to create a curtain around them.

"Look, you are grown and know what you're doing. I need to realize that—we all do. But if you're asking for advice, just consider this, okay? Regardless if it's Michael or another guy or whoever, it will never work out unless you let them love you. Every relationship—romantic or not—requires vulnerability, and there's always going to be something that feels unsurmountable. But if you love someone, you say they are something worth fighting for. And maybe he is or maybe he's not, but when you find that person, you need to be in 100 percent. Your fear will always win if you let it.

"And look, Dad might be hard to talk to about this, but talk to him now. Don't wait until you're in love and torn to find out. You don't know where he stands until you talk to him."

Leilani sniffled but nodded, knowing she had to talk to her father whether she wanted to or not.

"I'm not saying you need to tell Dad about Michael today. But start a conversation. Talk to Dad—talk to us. You have so many people who love you. I know, because your friends kept messaging me, trying to figure out if you were okay. You've left a lot of people in the dark. It's time to let some light in."

Leilani grabbed her sister, firmly hugging her, unable to find the words to thank her. They held each other until Makellah called Candice to check why they were taking so long.

Candice smiled at Leilani and lifted her chin up.

"Leilani and I were driving through some unfamiliar roads, but don't worry, I'm treating y'all with dinner. We'll be over soon with food."

***

Most of Thanksgiving week was spent in a fury of cooking, cleaning, and calming their father down; he continued to try to fix areas of the house after work to make it nicer for his guests. Between the kids running around, Aisha's husband chiding Leilani's father, and the sisters managing the house, the storm couldn't quiet the laughter, stories, and noise in their father's home.

But like the weather, the house soon left behind little evidence of what had transpired: one of the boy's forgotten coloring books, Aisha's leftovers prepackaged for their father to eat during the week, and one of Makellah's sweaters. With Zoë and her father remaining, Leilani heard the familiar silence she had grown to fear. She touched the locket around her neck, holding on to Candice's parting gift that encouraged her to stop and smell the roses. With deep breaths, she tried to calm herself.

She would wake up early for a run around the neighborhood, shower, work, and clean the house before reading or messaging Kat. Kat hadn't gone through her exact experiences, but she understood feeling very alone: she was caretaking her ailing grandmother before her eventual passing. Though Leilani felt comfortable speaking to Kat, she hadn't reached out to the rest of the friend group, afraid of being rejected for having gone MIA. At Kat's insistence, Leilani texted in the group chat, mentioned the breakup, and suggested a video call. No sooner had Leilani hit sent, her friends had scheduled a time to talk.

In her warmest oversized sweater, Leilani waited to see everyone slowly enter the meeting.

"Hi, guys. How's everyone?"

Brittany's screen froze before a delayed voice crackled through and her video feed turned black.

"Oh geez. She's going to have another shitty meeting. You should have seen her in October when we tried to bring her on, Leilani. Homegirl was sounding like an overenthusiastic Alexa—ugh no, shut up, I'm not talking to you—I hate these devices." Yet again, Kat began to fight with her smart devices.

"How's things in your neck of the woods, Kat? What projects are you work on?" Leilani was amazed how Kat could run on such little sleep and yet produce line after line of code. Kat's wavy hair protruded from her head at different directions, in part due to Kat's unwillingness to control her curls.

Kat shrugged. "Same old, same old. I'm constantly over-worked and tired of teaching the offshore team how to do their jobs. It's really not that hard. I even give them a cheat sheet and they still ping me. 'Kat, can you help me with this?' 'Kat, can you join a call?'"

Brittany's video feed came back, showing a close-up of her russet brown face in a clear attempt to find for the best signal in her house. After finding a solid connection, she adjusted the camera on her couch and showed off her new Ivy Park maroon jumpsuit.

"Um, Brit, you can't sit over there looking like a model and not expect me to get distracted. Drop a girl a link to your 'fit! But to answer your question, Leilani, I can't help them anymore. Oswaldo and Ernie are sweet. They mean well. But they shouldn't be in the programming department if they need this much hand-holding."

Brittany made a variety of faces before commenting. "I think Oswaldo and Ernie are hitting on their coworker."

Kat looked unimpressed. "They're both old enough to be my father. No, thank you. I don't have daddy issues, and I really enjoy not being harassed at work anymore."

Leilani leaned on her hand as she laid in bed. "I can't believe HR won't do anything. Again, for a company so cen-tered in hiring women, they suck at listening to the people they hire. You can't be surprised at why you lose so many women of color if your HR department won't deal with harassment claims!"

Kat shrugged again. "I'm honestly used to it. I'm the Latina in the room with curves. So clearly I'm asking for it, right?" She rolled her eyes. "This is why my dad sent me to martial arts classes when I was little. The guys stopped making crude comments in front of me after hearing I was a state champion in Judo."

"Doesn't stop them from doing it behind your back." Nia cocked her head to the right while pressing her lips together and raising her eyebrows.

Kat threw her hands up. "Hashtag 'Life in Corporate America.' Also, Nia, sorry to keep you in the lobby for so long—I didn't realize it wouldn't let you in immediately!"

Nia laughed. "I know goddamn well you were trying to keep me out. But anyway, we're here for you, Leilani."

"Right. So Leilani, tell us what happened." Kat had to pretend like the conversation was new to her, but she knew Leilani would get extra heat from Brittany and Nia if she revealed she hid information from them. Though after retelling the abortion, family meeting, and the breakup, her friends sensed there was something more.

"Fuck, I'm sorry Leilani. You were so into him. But you know, you were right. You should figure out how you feel about him. It wasn't right to lead him on, but damn, girl. Why didn't you tell us about the... procedure? We would have been here for you. It explains why you were MIA—I mean, I thought you were just *hella* sprung, but I understand it was also personal and—"

Kat jumped into Brittany's run-on sentence. "What Brittany is trying to say is we get it was rough—but fuck, tell us! We are here for you. Even if you go a little boy crazy for someone, don't forget we're here for you. We were there for your move-in day, we were there for our first suite-mate party when you puked your body weight out, and we were there for you when you had a mental breakdown before the O-chem exam. We might not have been your first pick at roommates, but we're here for you until the end. And we'll stand next to you at your wedding, regardless of who it's to. I'm basically telling you this because I don't want you to forget about us when you get a new boyfriend."

Leilani couldn't help to laugh as she wiped her tears away. "I know. Or maybe I didn't? I was just a complete wreck and I was scared as hell. And I didn't want you to think my family was racist, though I guess they kinda are even though we're Black?" She shook her head. "Okay, I don't really know how it all works out—I'll leave it to Nia to correct me, but I was scared. And this damn pandemic made me lose my head. I guess the positive side is I'm now focusing on being more open with people. I'm still in Texas, but I'm trying to talk to my dad more and understand him and his perspective more.

"I guess I've never taken the time to actually compare what I think he wants from me versus what he actually wants from me. I was putting a lot of extra pressure on myself unnecessarily."

"I think that mindset comes from you wanting to be there for everyone, even if it means you are not there for you," Nia began, nodding sympathetically. "My parents are children of Panamanian immigrants, but the fact I was the first to go to college and I'm an only child made it hard to do my own thing. Obviously, I'm oversimplifying, but I'm trying to get at the fact being the child of immigrants is difficult: you have to balance what you want out of life with your family's expectations. And you can't make everyone happy. But, I guess, I'm curious to know—what are you going to do? You said you broke it off because you were too unsure and it was leading him on, but… what now?"

"Well… I know how I feel," Leilani started. "And I can't hide my fear of everyone hating me as to why I pushed him away; from talking to my sisters and dad, the fear was obviously there, but they aren't going to cut me out of their lives. At least not outright. It was going to be a tough battle. But the more I talk to my dad about the end with my mom, he seems… less angry? I don't know, he is more level-headed than I expected him to be." She smiled. "He's a bit of a tornado, trying to please everyone while also being a disciplinarian. But he's older now and has an interesting perspective looking back. He recognizes *why* my mom left and he doesn't excuse it. He's starting to thank her for letting him be a part of her life, because it means he had his girls. So I guess that encourages me to forgive myself and to forgive Michael for not being exactly what I needed 100 percent of the time. Which was also unfair for me to put on him.

"I guess I'm trying to say I'd love to have him back, but I don't know if he would even want me back. I don't even know how to talk to him. I haven't messaged him since before I left, and I shipped his stuff to his apartment. What do I say? Or do?"

The girls looked frozen, and Leilani feared the bandwidth was unable to handle the weight of it all.

Until Brittany spoke.

"Well, what would you say? If he were here?"

"I don't know. I started to write letters to him during the pandemic, but I stopped in the last two months or so… I even tried to write down how I felt, but I couldn't figure it out. I think I'm too afraid to put pen to paper—it feels like once I do, it will really feel over."

Kat shifted in her seat. "I don't know how comfortable you are with this or if you still have it, but maybe write it down and send him the letters you wrote? He might be willing to come back if you show him how you really feel."

Everyone seemed to think it was a good idea and encouraged Leilani to send it as a "last Christmas" gift. She felt good about it, but...

"What if he doesn't say yes?"

Kat gave a sad smile. "Then we'll be here for you."

Nia smiled and sent her an old picture of them in their dorm, proudly displaying an old school fort made up of blankets and pillows. "And we'll all marry each other and retire together in Florida."

Brittany laughed and sent a meme of elderly ladies sitting on a rocker and drinking beers.

After recovering from the fit of laughter, Kat shrugged and said, "Fuck it—at least you tried. Instead of wondering 'what if,' right? It doesn't matter what he says—this is about you. And you getting closure. Think of it as a reverse burning of a lover's letter. And if he burns it, you're free. And if he comes back to you, he's yours. A potential temporary disappointment for a lifetime of relief."

Leilani laughed and nodded. She texted Joanna before she lost her nerve, asking her for one last favor before she was disowned by Michael's entire family.

"Alright," she said. "I'll do it."

DEC. 3

Biden said he will ask Americans to wear masks for 100 days.

DEC. 18

The F.D.A. approved Moderna's Covid vaccine.

DEC. 11

The F.D.A. approved a vaccine by Pfizer

DEC. 14

The U.S. death toll surpassed 300,000.

The U.K. approved Pfizer's coronavirus vaccine.

Jan. 20

President Biden Issues New COVID-19 Guidance

Jan. 25

U.S. Cases of COVID-19 Surpass 25 Million

DEC. 8

The U.K. began vaccinations

DEC. 2

The U.K. approved Pfizer's coronavirus vaccine.

Winter 2021
A Timeline of the Coronavirus Pandemic

Total US Confirmed COVID-19 Cases on January 31th, 2021: 26,220,001
Death Count on January 31th, 2021: 441,299

100,000 COVID-19 Deaths in the United States

Jan. 20

January 22

New Data Shows Moderna Vaccine Can Induce
Rare Anaphylactic Reactions

CDC Estimates COVID-19 Vaccinations Have Surpassed 25 Million in the United States

Jan. 28

Jan. 13

CDC Estimates COVID-19 Vaccinations Have Surpassed 10 Million First Doses in the United States

DEC. 20

London entered a severe lockdown, ordered by Boris Johnson.

EPILOGUE

———

LEILANI, EMERYVILLE

Postmarked: January 2, 2021
From: Michael Boutros
Chicago, Illinois

Leilani—
Joanna told me everything.
And now, I'm stuck with a journal full of love notes I've read and reread a thousand times. I've been obsessing over it. And how can I not? It's you.
But it's also not fair for you to bring this to me now.
So now I have to get things off my chest too.
While you were away in Texas, I was worried about you. And tried not to bother you so much. I didn't want to be clingy, but getting to see you was worth rushing through work all day. I just wanted to see and hear you. I understand maybe you weren't in that place yet. I tried to also force myself to not think that way or get ahead of myself.

But it killed me. I stand by what I said. It was your choice. But if life were different, I would have begged you to keep it. I would beg you to stay with me. I would beg you to give me a chance to treat you like the queen you are and show you I can make it great, even if you weren't sure.

But if life were different, I would also not be begging. Because you would love me too.

How can I blame you for not loving me as much as I loved you? That's not fair to you. I know that. So I tried to better myself. Because if I was lucky enough, I might have another chance with you, and I didn't want to mess it up.

Well, it's messed up.

And I'm not sure what I did wrong. But I know it hurts a lot.

I can't help but wonder what I could have done better. And maybe it's egoistical to think that way, but when you really wanted something to work out, it's human nature to doubt yourself, your self-worth, your reason for being. I think I must have truly loved you, because throughout all of this, despite how mad, how frustrated, how disappointed I've been with you, I still love you.

And I would still fight for you.

Our relationship has never lacked love.

So it makes it harder for me to do this.

I'm sorry. I can't go through this again. I don't think I could survive another loss.

Leilani, I love you, but I ask you don't try to reach out about getting back together.

While you were away, I realized how many things weren't going right. How many things I pushed you into doing because I wanted you to do them.

I see why you wrote so many of these letters to me. It makes it easier to tell you what I need when I'm not looking at your beautiful brown eyes and trying not to melt and acquiesce. But now I'm scared to stop writing. Because the moment I put my pen down, it means I have to walk away from you…

Michael

BELEN, LOS ANGELES
January 16, 2021

Dear Belen Yackeline de León,
Congratulations! I am delighted to make you this conditional offer of admission to the MSc in International Relations for the 2021/2022 session as a full-time student. Please note this decision is authoritative and official only when you receive it in writing from the Graduate Admissions Office. You can also find details of your offer via the online tracker.

As a full-time student, you will be required to attend a minimum of twenty-one hours of study per week, beginning September 24, 2021. Registration is on September 21, 2021. If you are required to attend an introductory course, details will be below. The programme lasts twelve months, finishing September 25, 2022. The graduation ceremony will be in December following completion of the programme.

LSE Financial Support
I am delighted to inform you you have been given a partial Graduate Support Scheme (GSS) Award. Please go to the applicant portal to review your financial award.

Preparation for Your Arrival

Registration starts in September, although you may have pre-sessional requirements that mean you need to register early—your specific registration date is stated above. There is plenty of information about arriving at the school and what to do in your first weeks here in the Offer Pack, and any additional updates will be published online at LSE.ac.uk/YourFirstWeeks during the summer.

We look forward to welcoming you to LSE at the start of your programme.

Head of Admissions at London School of Economics

PRISCILA FUENTES, TUCSON
Priscila Fuentes, January 21, 1994–October 19, 2020
Survived by her loving parents, Amy Chu-Fuentes and Alvaro Fuentes, and her brother, Vincent Fuentes

Eulogy Transcript Starts:

Before I tell you about how special Priscila was, I would like to take this opportunity to thank all of you for being here today. Your show of support has been overwhelming, and I am not sure how we would have gotten through the last few weeks without all of you. Thank you for the meals you have delivered, the help with organizing the services, and the outpouring of love you have shown.

This has been the worst time of my life, in our family's lives, but you have helped us get through it. Thank you from the bottom of my heart.

Sorry, please give me a moment.

Priscila was born on January 21, 1994, in Los Angeles.

We were moving to Arizona and trying to get everything settled in our new home, but as always Priscila was one step ahead. She was strong-willed and quiet, even as a child. When she grew older, it was obvious she was very smart and had an interest in how things worked. She always said, "I like bugs. People are complicated to figure out. But I understand why bugs move and do things." And so she swore she was going to pursue a career in STEM—something different from the family. Priscila had an eye for everything. I like to think that's why she was so well versed in so many things. She was an incredible photographer, a great violinist, and a phenomenal white hat hacker. I told Amy, "She's going to do something important. She's our little star." It's why we named her Priscila—she was going to be a great leader and make an impact.

She didn't see it. I don't think Priscila really saw it until... right before she passed.

Priscila had this dream to retire in France. She knew her uncle, my brother, had passed from a terrible respiratory disease and had always wanted to see Paris. She wanted to live the dream for him. She worked year after year to save up and live there permanently. That was her dream—to live out his.

In one of the last conversations I had with her before she started to lose consciousness, she told me she understood why her uncle asked for Paris. It wasn't for him. It was for the family to look toward a better place, to find a place that would make them feel closer to him. And enjoy the beauty of what life was. And so, she told me to look for her in Vancouver, where they were handling the virus much better than France. Even while sick, she was cheeky.

As a healer, I deal with a lot of death.

But I find myself unable to find a phrase or religious verse that truly gives me solace. The only thing that helps me keep going is knowing while I'm alive, her memory continues, and by virtue, she lives.

She is a star who shined too bright. But it's because of her actions, her light, she has saved hundreds of people in the clinic, helping us care for as many people as possible. Our hearts weigh heavy every day she's not here with us.

Especially a day like today. Her twenty-seventh birthday. It's not natural for a parent to bury their child. But she decided she would do what she could to make sure no other parent would bury their children because of this pandemic.

I don't have words to help you cope with her death. But I'll end it with this.

Hold your loved ones a little closer.

Kiss them every day and night, even if you're mad.

Call whoever you've been angry with or if you've had disputes. Because you'll never get a chance to know when they'll be gone.

Fix things before they're too late.

And if you have children, for my Priscila, please tell them you love them.

I wished I had told her that more often. I wish I held her more often. I wish I could have protected her from all of this. El hubiera no si existe. "What if" doesn't exist.

Take it from one grieving father who loved his daughter—love as much as you can and hold your loved ones tight.

Thank you.

Eulogy Transcription Ends

ACKNOWLEDGMENTS

———

It's been quite a journey writing this book. It almost didn't happen, but the supporters below made this book a reality.

To all of my friends and family who encouraged my writing process, edited my words, and kept me going, I am forever grateful.

Papá y Mamá, sin ustedes, no estuviera donde estoy. Este libro fue frustrante, difícil and uno de los triunfos mas grandes de mi vida. Este libro es nuestro logro. Los amo con todo mi corazón y estoy tan agradecida por tenerlos como mis mas grandes héroes.

Christopher, I laugh in awe at the rollercoaster ride I've put you through. We not only lived through a pandemic together, but we survived this book writing process. You deserve more than a few rounds of applause. You saw it all: the insecurity, the fear, the worries, and the panic. There would be no book without your patience, love, and willingness to hold me up when I wanted to quit. I can't wait to do this again with book number two.

Kristin, Ari, and Alex, I can't fathom writing this book without you three. You heard my late-night rants and kept my sanity and well-being in check every step of the way. Thank you so much for being the incredible human beings you are. Elise and Dominique, you were the first people who made room for me to dream big and lead. I aspire to be the kind of mentor you both have been to me. You are the women I look up to, and I am so lucky to work and know you. Thank you for always being there for me.

James, Nick, and Christian, you have all been a consistent voice of reason, a trusted advisor, and an inspiration. You've known me since I was a freshman in college and have mentored me into the early stages of my professional career. Thank you for always supporting me and being one of my biggest advocates in every turn of my life.

Missy, Christine, Cinthya, and Deb, this book is a product of your vocation: educating, advising, and supporting first generation college students like myself. Thanks to you, I have the opportunity to pay it forward with other students and help the next generation. Thanks to you all, I have a voice. Thanks to you, I've been able to make my dream a reality.

This book was made possible also by a community of people who believed in me so fervently they preordered their copies and helped promote the book before it even went to print. I'd like to gratefully acknowledge:

Kristin Richards

Dominique Rougeau

Elise Cornille

Miguel A. Chigüindo

Reyna de Chigüindo

James Patrick Kelly

Alex Garvey

George Duffy

Darren Sanders

Carrie Gan

Coline Cazoulat

Linda Zanella

Grace Morgan

Sara Odisho

Nick Wertsch
Peter Soh
Raphael Roman
Ari Newsome
Elsa Lazo-Vasquez
Daisy Peraza
Camille Ruddick
Gloria Garvey
Cinthya Salazar
Florence Kong
Ringo TsunHo
Quinlan Hampton
Francis Sam
Sabrina Rodriguez
Lilia Tkach
Noemi Ibarra
Ashlee Avery
John Caldas
Liz Jamae
Erika Marshall
Rebecca Cassidy
Alberto Morales
Nikki Parnala
Carl Powell Jr
Renzo Reyes
Eloy Cano

Do Kyung Yun
Albert Lee
Kayleigh Arcos
Priscilla Nguyen
Zeke Gutierrez
Alyssa Perez
Christine Pfeil
Viviana Jaramillo
Shannique Gibson
Isaac Franco
Sergio Perez
Vannessa Landaverry
Serena Lo
Dimitri Zabelin
Katherine Louie
Oriana Branon
Briana Megid
Deb Coburn
Maia Jin
Daniel Wiley
Katy Ahern
Eric Wong
Marlene DeFrates
Christian Arana
Daniela Ukuni
Tammy Olobo

I'd also like to give a special acknowledgment to those who have given this book, and the stories within it, legs strong enough to move forward. They not only supported my pre-sale book campaign but also heavily contributed feedback to craft this novel into its published form:

Ryan Keawekane, Krystal Galvis, Gabriela Wijegunawardena, Christopher Odisho, Alondra Medina, Eric Koester, Brian Bies, Clayton Bohle, Kristin Gustafson, and the publishing and editing team at New Degree Press. "Thank you" will never be enough. These stories were crafted from experiences my friends and I lived through as second generation immigrants and greatly inspired by the following novels:

- *A Handbook to Luck* by Cristina García
- *What We Lose* by Zinzi Clemmons
- *The Woman Warrior* by Maxine Hong Kingston
- *The Immortalists* by Chloe Benjamin

To all who contributed to the development of this novel's storylines, *gracias por las joyas prestadas.*

APPENDIX

———

INTRODUCTION

Cohen, Steve M. "Due Process: If It's Not Written, It Didn't Happen." *Psychology Today,* June 14, 2013. https://www.psychologytoday.com/us/blog/worked-work/201306/due-process-if-it-s-not-written-it-didn-t-happen.

Cole, Diane. "Why Scapegoating Is a Typical Human Response to a Pandemic." *NPR.* August 29, 2020. https://www.npr.org/sections/goatsandsoda/2020/08/29/906225199/why-scapegoating-is-a-typical-human-response-to-a-pandemic.

Duckworth, Angela Lee. "Grit: The Power of Passion and Perseverance." Filmed April 2013, TED video, 6:01. https://www.ted.com/talks/angela_lee_duckworth_grit_the_power_of_passion_and_perseverance/up-next?language=en

Pew Research Center. "Second-Generation Americans." Social & Demographic Trends Project. February 7, 2013. Accessed March 1, 2021. https://www.pewresearch.org/social-trends/2013/02/07/second-generation-americans/

Pollak, Susan M. "Do Pandemics Kill Compassion?" *Psychology Today*. March 20, 2020. https://www.psychologytoday.com/us/blog/the-art-now/202003/do-pandemics-kill-compassion.

White, Gillian B. and National Journal. "How Black Middle-Class Kids Become Poor Adults." *The Atlantic*, February 8, 2015. https://www.theatlantic.com/business/archive/2015/02/how-black-middle-class-kids-become-poor-adults/425253/.

BELEN, LOS ANGELES, AUGUST 2020

DuPree, Will, and Russell Falcon. "Army Investigator Claims 'No Credible Reports' Vanessa Guillen Was Sexually Harassed before Her Disappearance." *KXAN Austin*. July 03, 2020. https://www.kxan.com/news/texas/fort-hood-senior-commander-provides-update-on-investigation-into-vanessa-guillens-disappearance/.

CHAPTER DIVIDERS

Fraser. "Timeline of Events Related to the COVID-19 Pandemic." Accessed April 15, 2021. https://fraser.stlouisfed.org/timeline/covid-19-pandemic#158

Taylor, Derrick Bryson. "A Timeline of the Coronavirus Pandemic." *New York Times*, March 17, 2021. https://www.nytimes.com/article/coronavirus-timeline.html

The New York Times. "Coronavirus in the U.S.: Latest Map and Case Count." Accessed April 15, 2021. https://www.nytimes.com/interactive/2020/us/coronavirus-us-cases.html

Made in the USA
Las Vegas, NV
14 October 2021